Horizons Mathematics 1

Book 1

by
Sareta A. Cummins

Edited by
David J. Korecki

Illustrated by
Tye A. Rausch

Editorial Staff
Christine A. Korecki
John P. Robinett

Revisions
Alan Christopherson
Chris Burkholder
Annette Walker

Alpha Omega Publications, Inc.
Rock Rapids, IA

Horizons Mathematics 1, Book 1 is only a *part* of a mathematics curriculum which consists of Horizons Mathematics 1, Book 1; Horizons Mathematics 1, Book 2; and Horizons Mathematics 1 Teacher's Guide. It is *necessary* to use the Teacher's Guide for a complete first grade mathematics program. The Teacher's Guide contains some essential concepts that are not presented in the student workbooks.

Horizons Mathematics 1, Book 1

804 N. 2nd Ave. E., Rock Rapids, IA 51246-1759

Printed in the United States of America

ISBN 978-1-58095-923-0

Horizons

Mathematics 1

NUMBERS

① **Trace the numbers.**

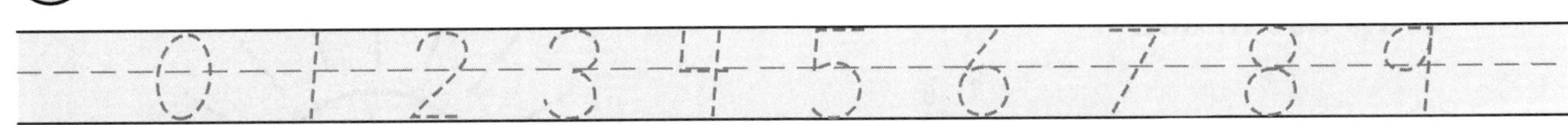

② **Write numbers 0–9.**

③ **Write in the missing numbers on the number line.**

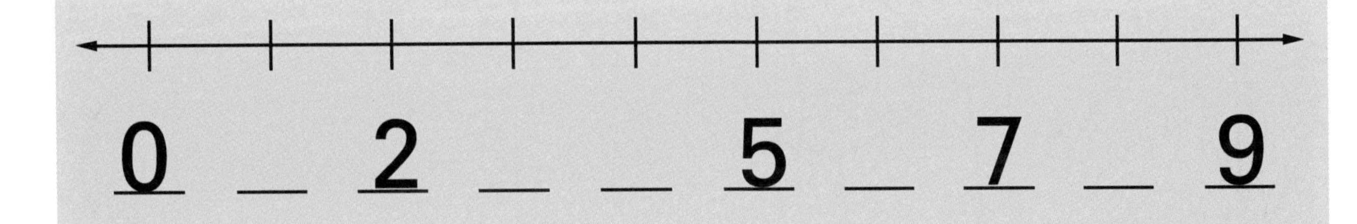

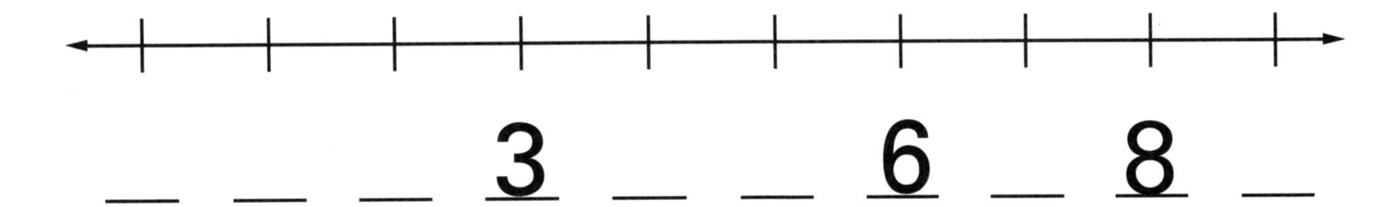

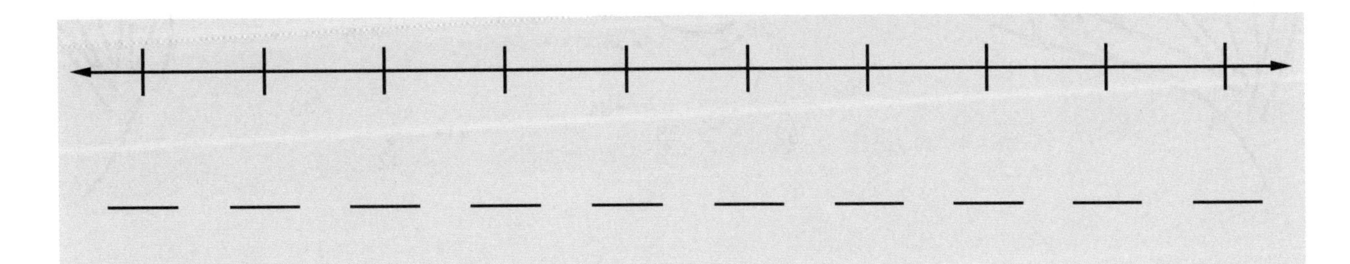

4 Connect the dots.

Draw dot to dot.

NUMBER ORDER – ORDINAL NUMBERS

1

God used numbers to put the world in order.

2 **Look at the numbers on the sailboats. These numbers show order. Count the sailboats.**

3 **Put an X on the first (1) sailboat.
Circle the fifth (5) sailboat.**

4. **Count the balls. Put an X on the third (3) ball. Circle the eighth (8) ball.**

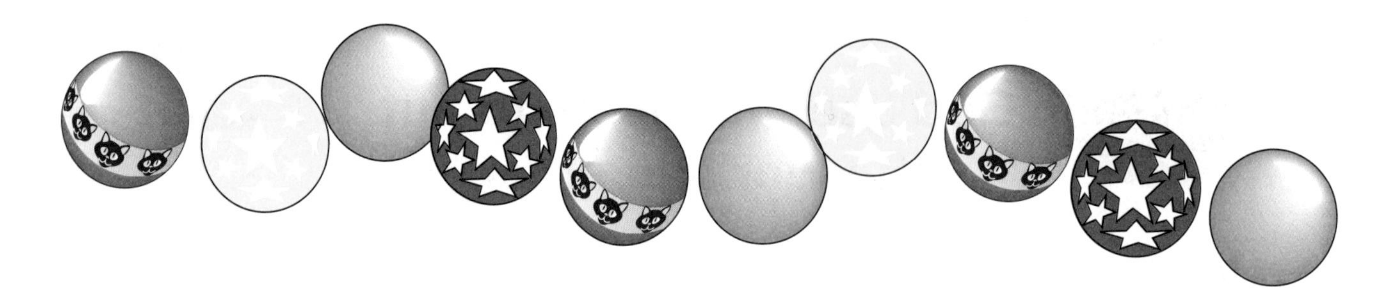

5. **Count the fish. Put an X on the second (2) fish.**

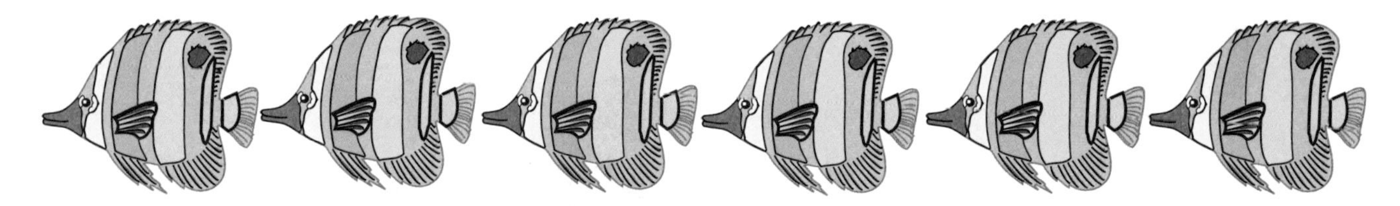

6. **Write the missing numbers.**

0 ___ ___ 3 ___ ___ ___ 7 ___ ___

___ 1 ___ ___ ___ ___ 6 ___ ___ ___

7. **Write the numbers in order.**

8 5 7 6	4 6 3 5
___ ___ ___ ___	___ ___ ___ ___

SETS

1 **Write the numbers 0–9.**

2 **Draw a set of 5 X's.** **Draw a set of 10 circles.**

3 **Write the missing numbers by 1's.**

1 ___ ___ 4 ___ 6 7

8 ___ 10 ___ 12 13 ___

15 ___ ___ 18 ___ 20 ___

4 **Write the missing numbers on the number line.**

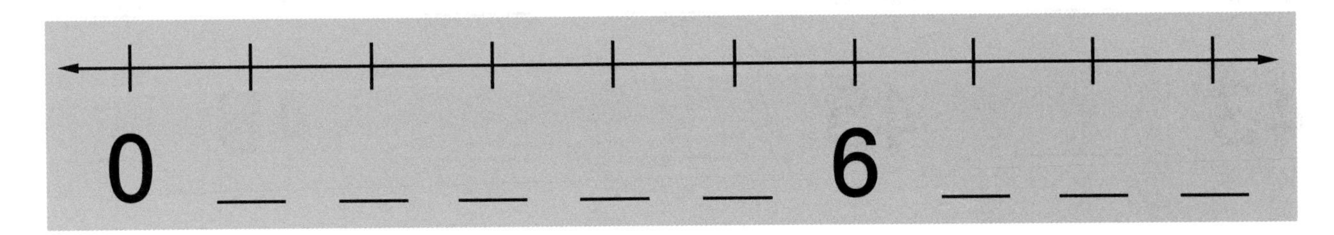

5. **Count the objects in each set. Write the number in the box.**

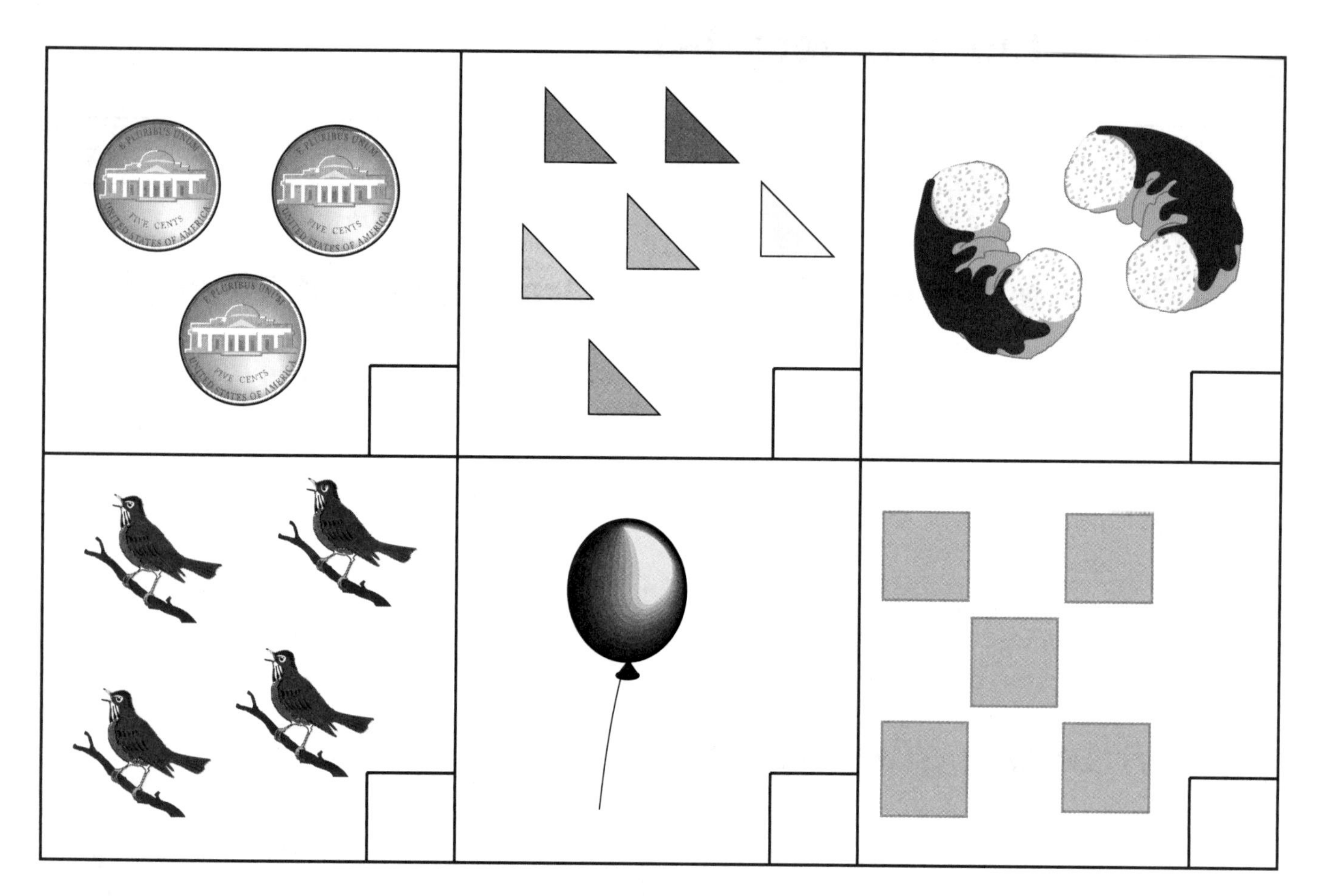

6. **Write the missing numbers by 1's.**

22	23	___	___	___	27	___
29	___	31	___	___	34	___
36	___	38	___	___	41	___
43	___	45	___	___	48	___

BIG AND LITTLE

① **Circle the bigger object.**

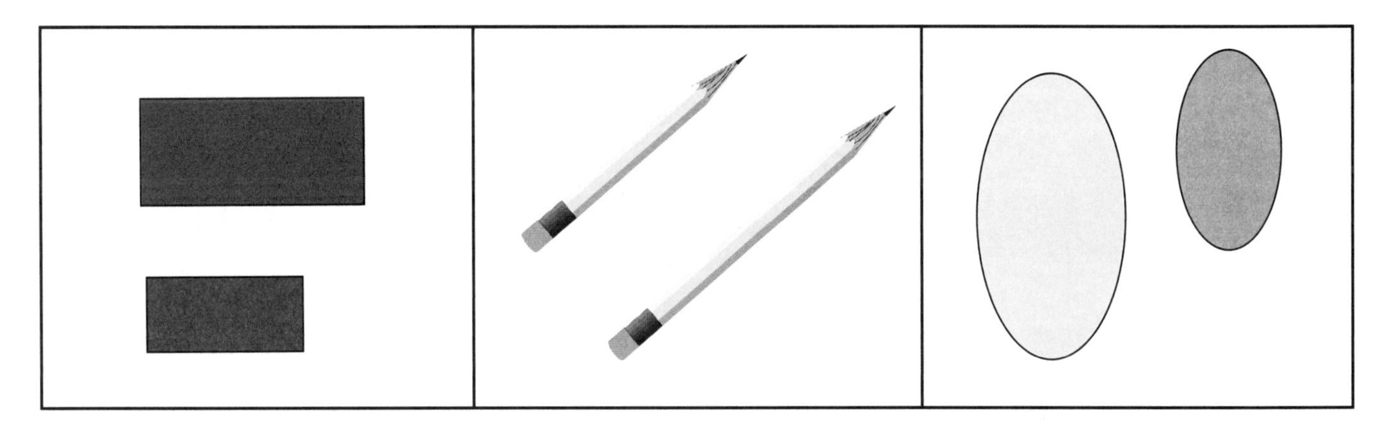

② **Circle the littler object.**

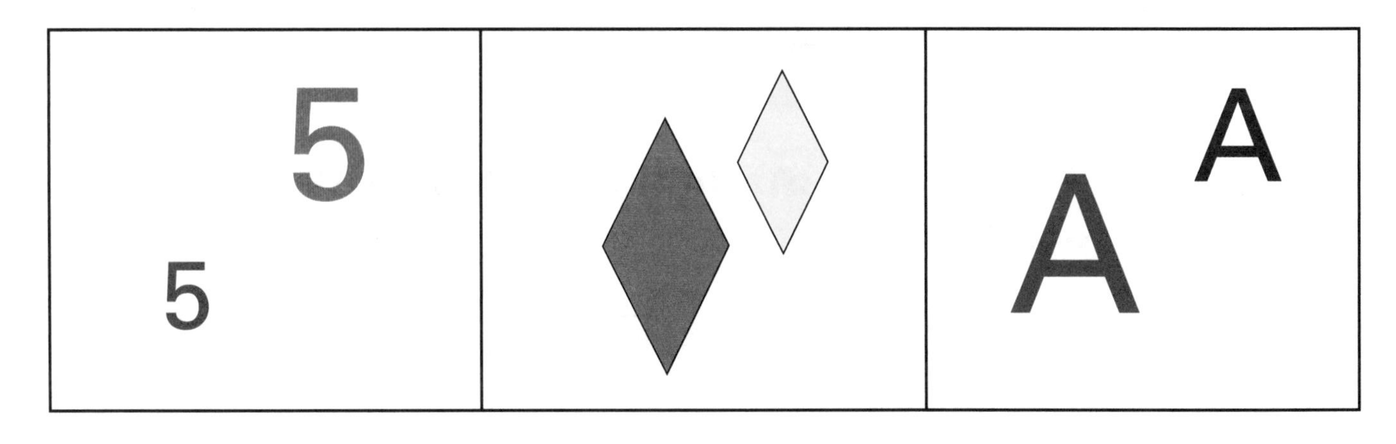

③ **Write the numbers in order.**

8 6 9 7

___ ___ ___ ___

16 17 15 14

___ ___ ___ ___

④ **Draw a set of 3 sticks. Draw a set of 9 balls.**

⑤ **Write the number that comes between.**

6 ___ 8   9 ___ 11   5 ___ 7

13 ___ 15   24 ___ 26   38 ___ 40

⑥ **Count the objects in each set. Write the number in the box.**

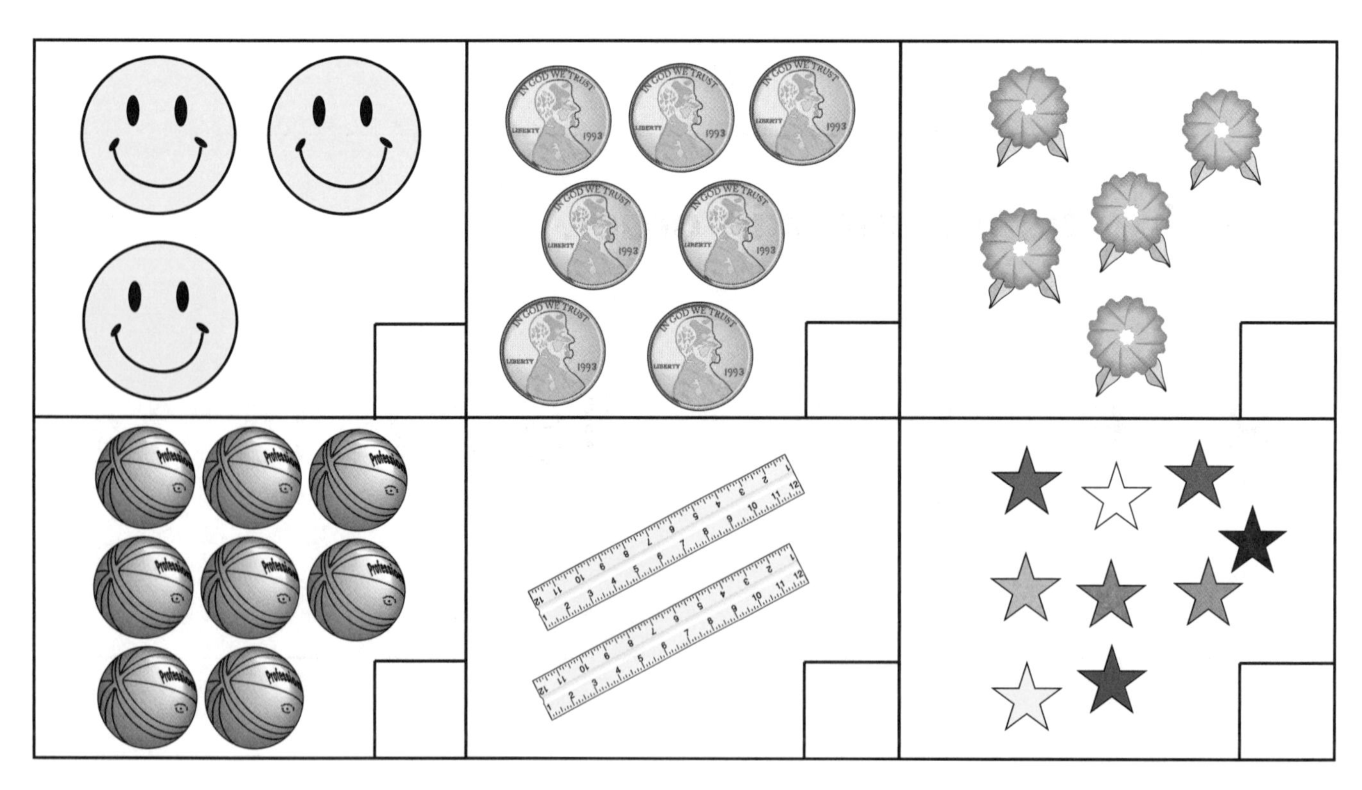

PLACE VALUE – TENS AND ONES

1 **The number 35 has two places. The 3 is in the tens' place. The 5 is in the ones' place.**

tens' place ones' place
3 5

The number 35 means:

tens' place ones' place

three groups of ten — five ones

The number 53 means:

tens' place ones' place

five groups of ten — three ones

2 **Count the groups of tens and ones. Write the numbers on the lines.**

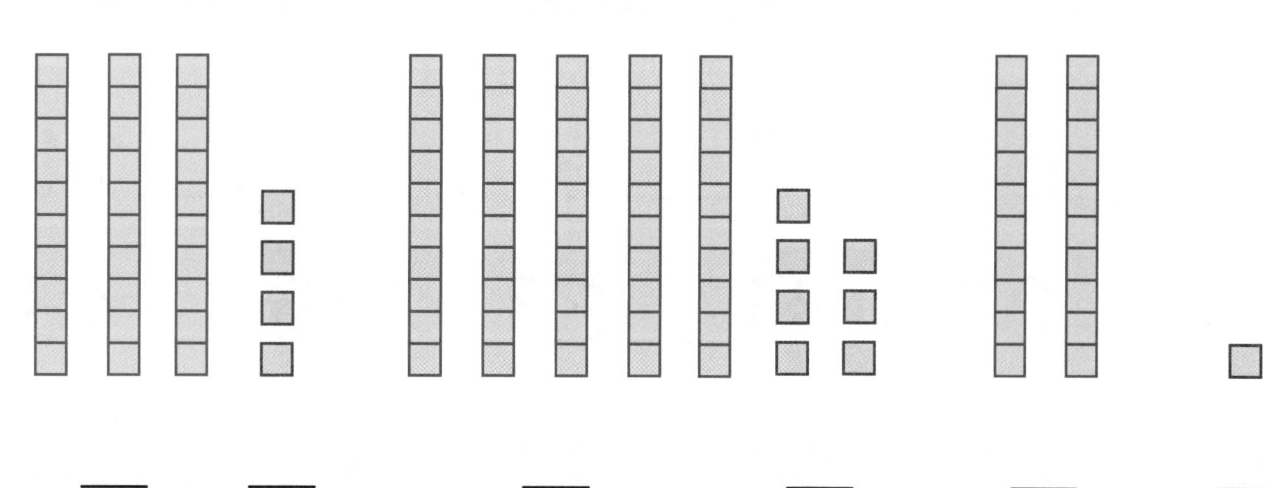

___ tens ___ ones   ___ tens ___ ones   ___ tens ___ ones

3. **Count the groups of tens and ones. Write the numbers on the lines.**

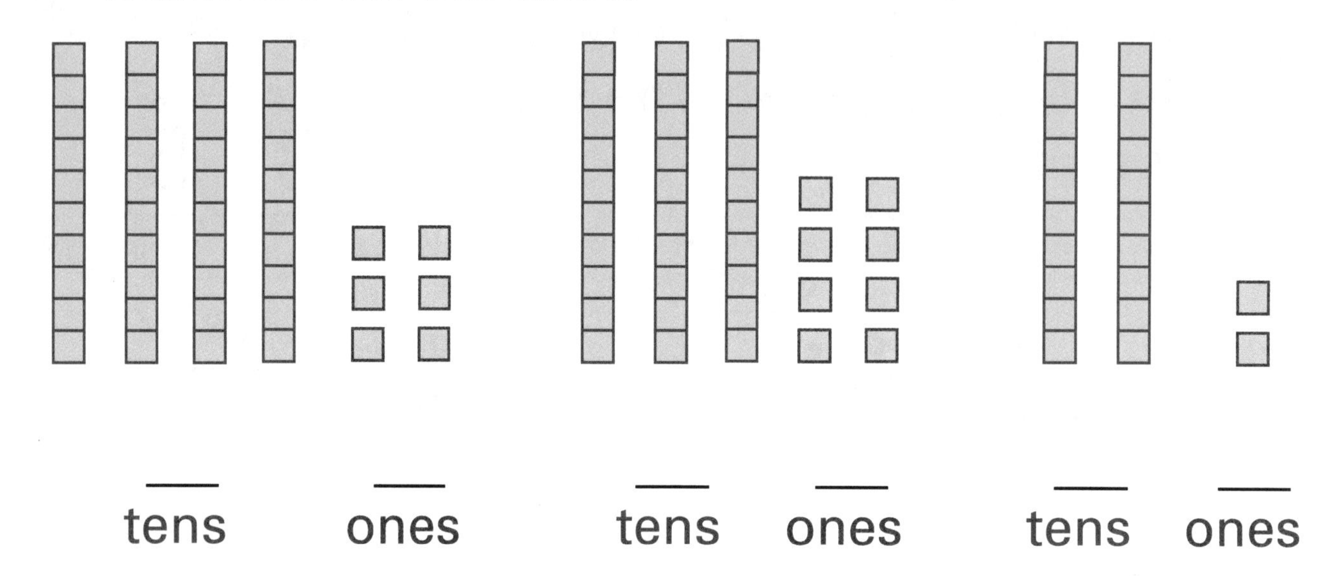

4. **Write the missing numbers when counting by 10's.**

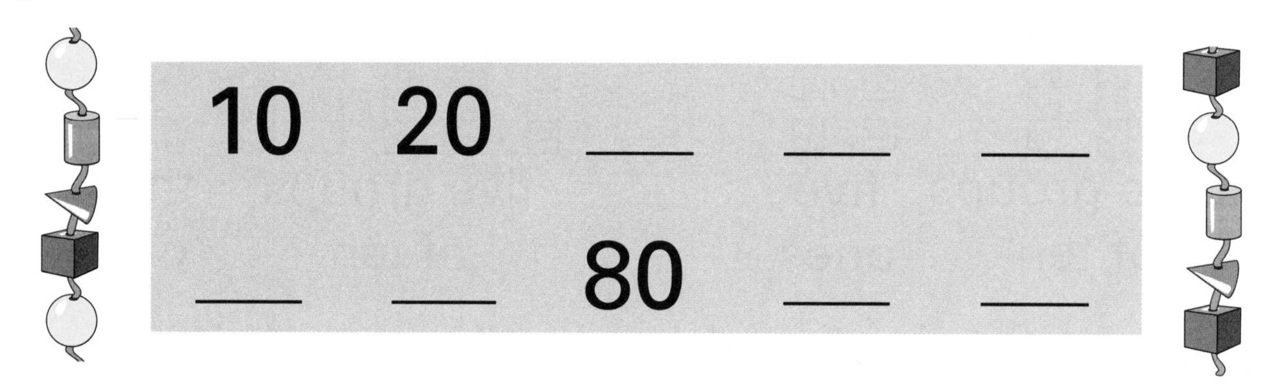

5. **Write the missing number that comes between.**

4 ___ 6	7 ___ 9	12 ___ 14
25 ___ 27	31 ___ 33	46 ___ 48
52 ___ 54	63 ___ 65	74 ___ 76

LESS AND GREATER

① **Circle the number that is less.**

5 6	2 9	2 0
7 4	3 1	5 8

② **Circle the number that is greater.**

1 7	1 5	5 3
8 0	2 3	6 8

③ **Circle the third teddy bear. Put an X on the sixth teddy bear. Put a box around the ninth teddy bear.**

④ **Write the numbers in order.**

10 6 9 7 11 5 8

____ ____ ____ ____ ____ ____ ____

5 Count the tens. Count the ones. Write the number.

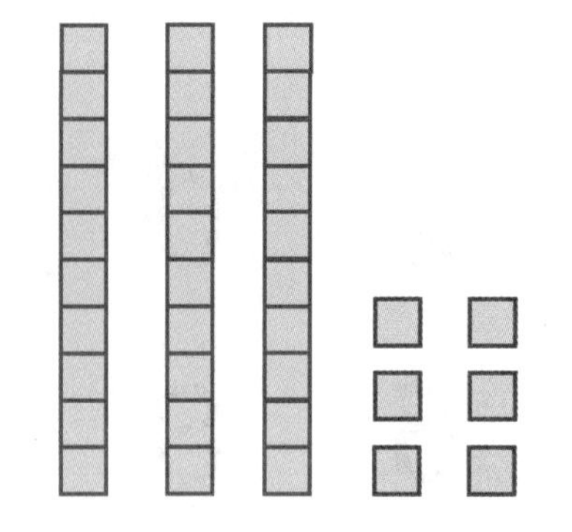

___tens ___ones

_____

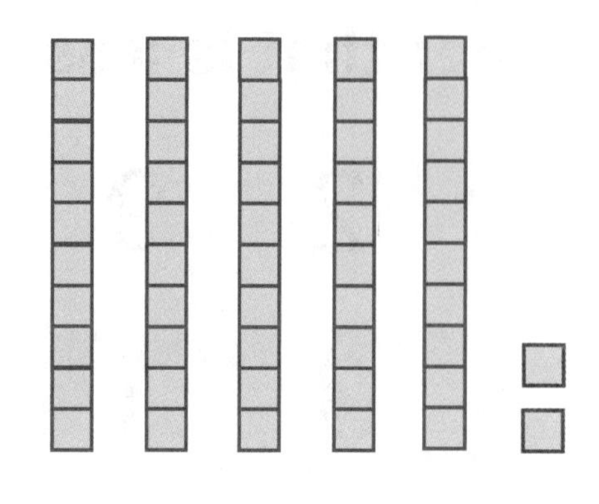

___tens ___ones

_____

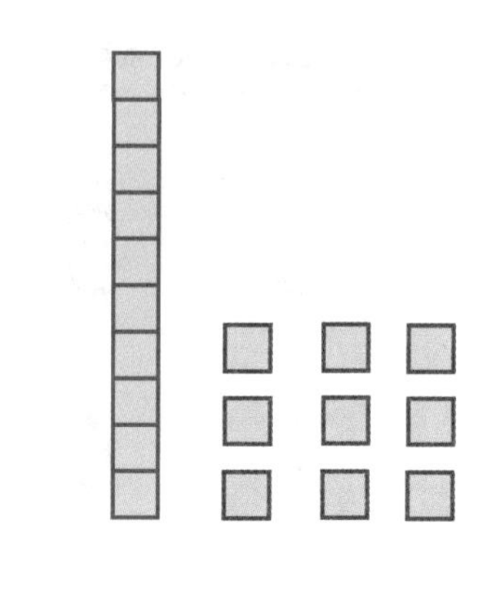

___tens ___ones

_____

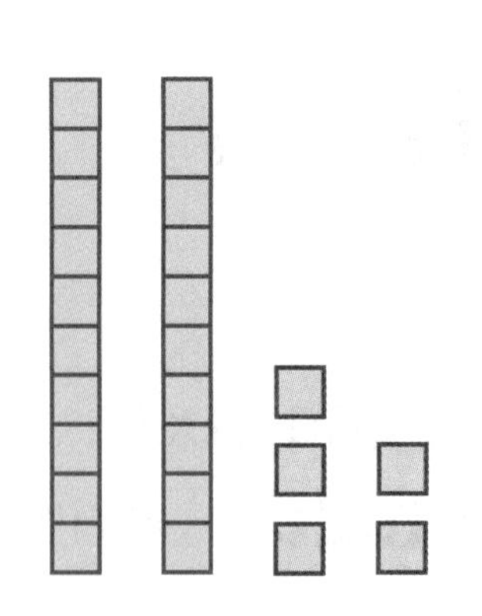

___tens ___ones

_____

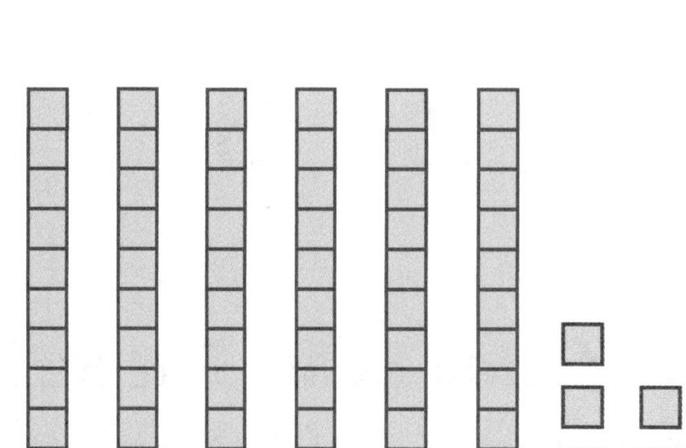

___tens ___ones

_____

___tens ___ones

_____

6 Write the missing numbers by 5's.

5 10 ___ ___ 25 ___ 35

40 ___ ___ 55 ___ ___ 70

ADDITION 1-9

① **Write the answer to these addition facts using the number line.**

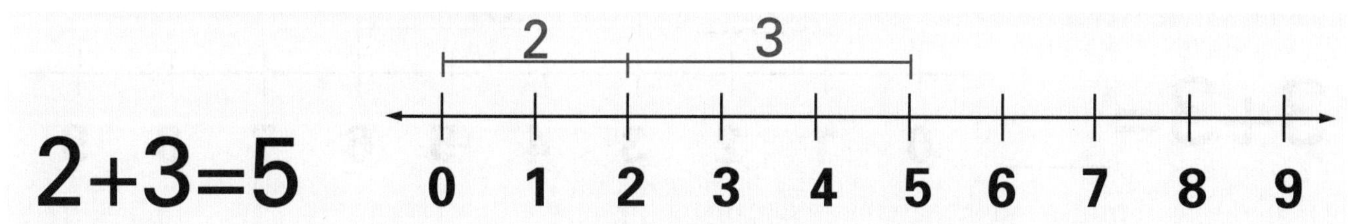

2+3=5

4 2
0 1 2 3 4 5 6 7 8 9

4+2=___

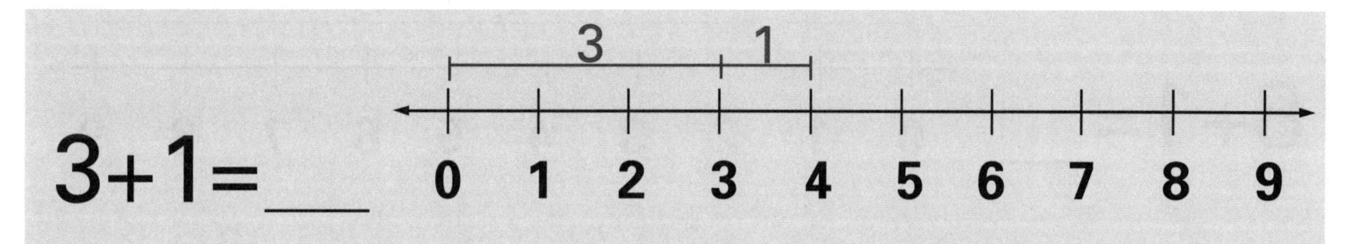

3+1=___

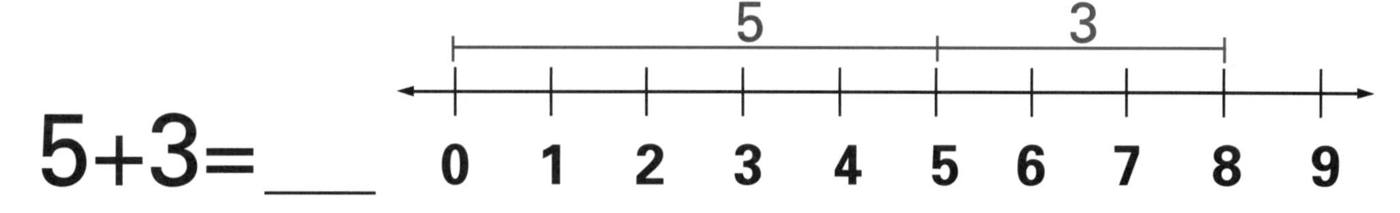

5+3=___

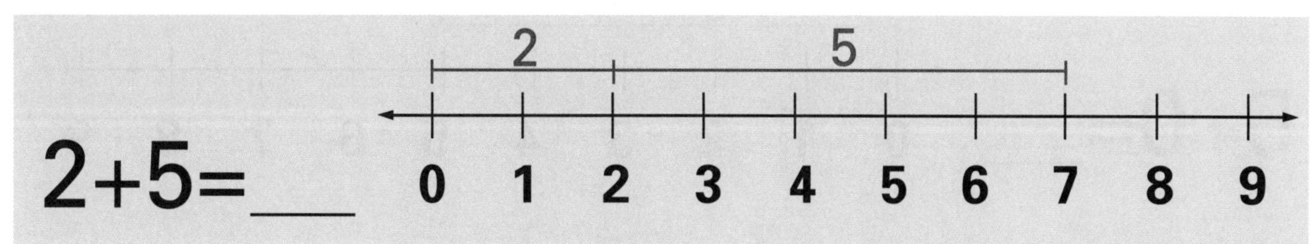

2+5=___

4 4
0 1 2 3 4 5 6 7 8 9

4+4=___

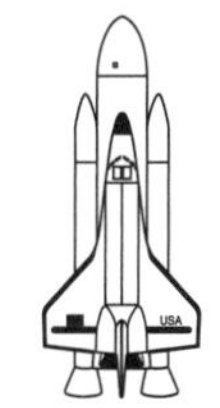

5+4=___

0	1	2	3	4	5	6	7	8	9

(5, 4)

3+3=___

0	1	2	3	4	5	6	7	8	9

(3, 3)

1+6=___

0	1	2	3	4	5	6	7	8	9

(1, 6)

8+1=___

0	1	2	3	4	5	6	7	8	9

(8, 1)

6+3=___

0	1	2	3	4	5	6	7	8	9

(6, 3)

5+0=___

0	1	2	3	4	5	6	7	8	9

(5)

3+2=___

0	1	2	3	4	5	6	7	8	9

(3, 2)

② **Read out loud.**

< means less than

> means greater than

$3 < 7$	$6 > 1$	$2 < 6$
$2 < 4$	$9 > 4$	$1 < 8$
$5 < 8$	$7 > 3$	$9 > 5$

③ **Write the missing numbers, counting by 1's.**

6 ___ 8   8 ___ 10   4 ___ 6

12 ___ 14   18 ___ 20   26 ___ 28

④ **Count the groups of ten by 10's. Count the ones. Write the number.**

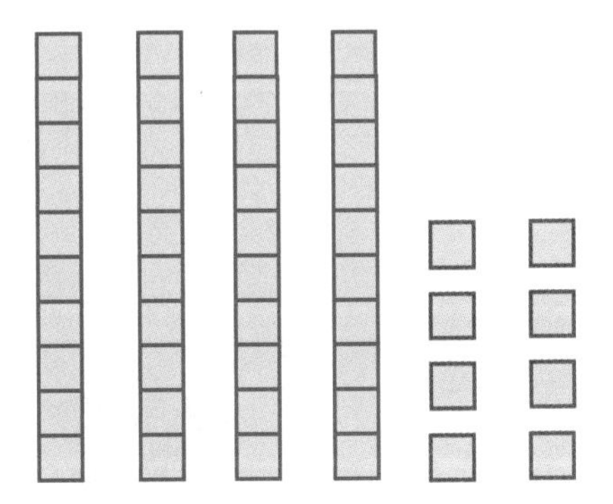

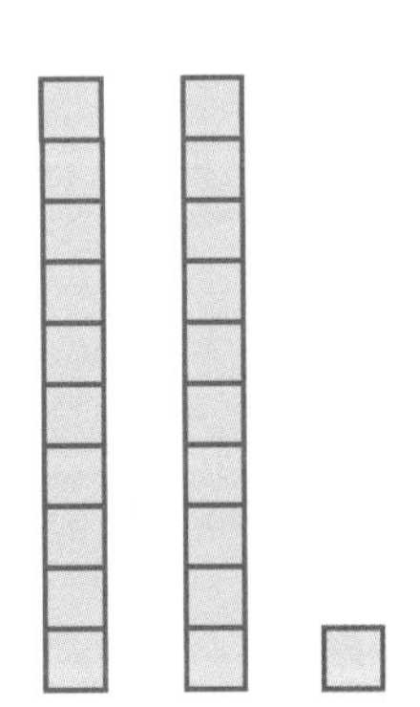

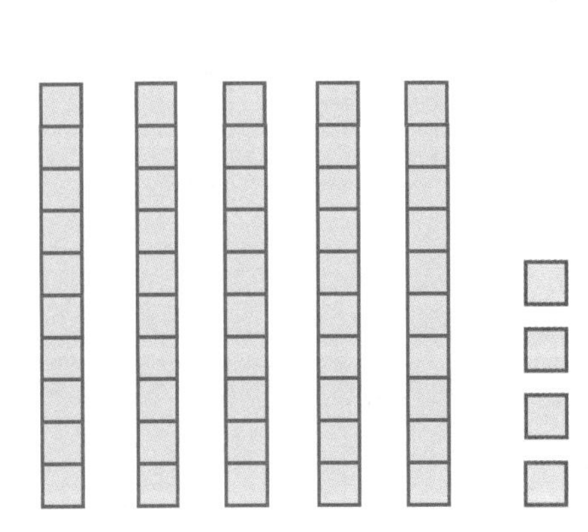

___   ___   ___

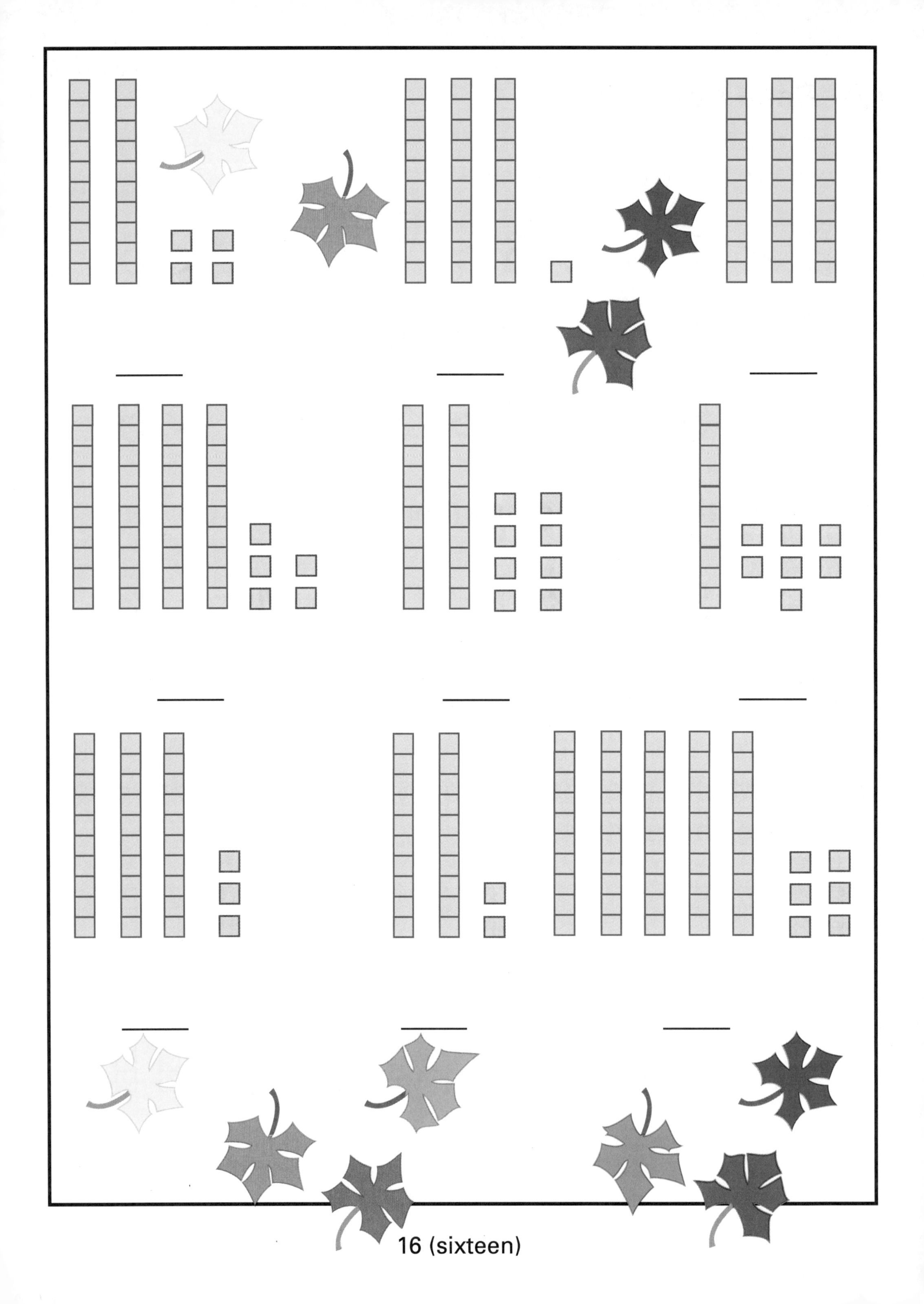

LARGE AND SMALL

① Circle the larger object.

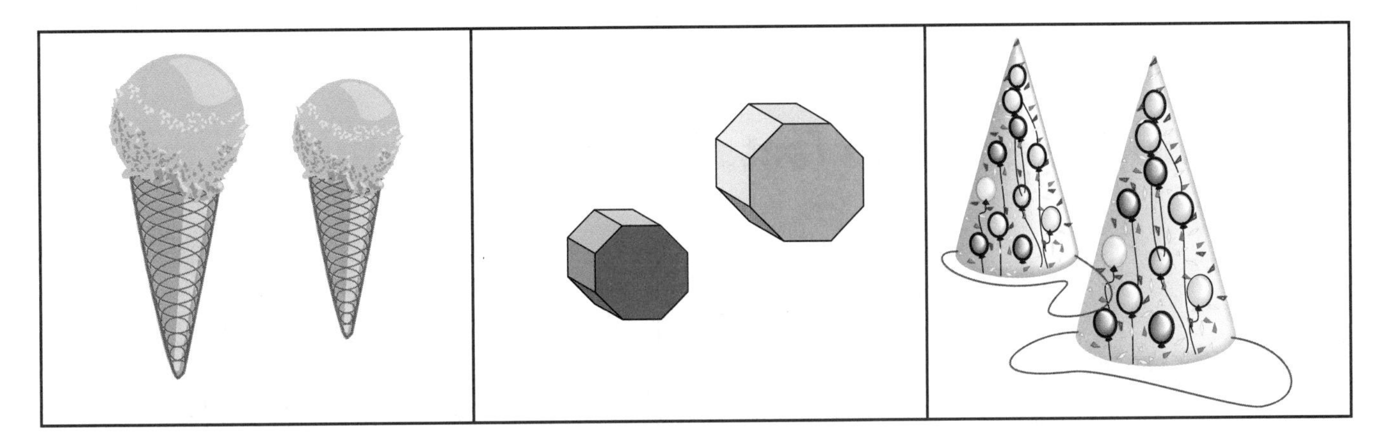

② Circle the smaller object.

③ Write the number of tens and ones.

72 = ____ tens+ ____ ones   28 = ____ tens+ ____ ones

57 = ____ tens+ ____ ones   46 = ____ tens+ ____ ones

35 = ____ tens+ ____ ones   64 = ____ tens+ ____ ones

12 = ____ ten + ____ ones   23 = ____ tens + ____ ones

38 = ____ tens + ____ ones   81 = ____ tens + ____ one

④ **Write the addition fact shown on the number line.**

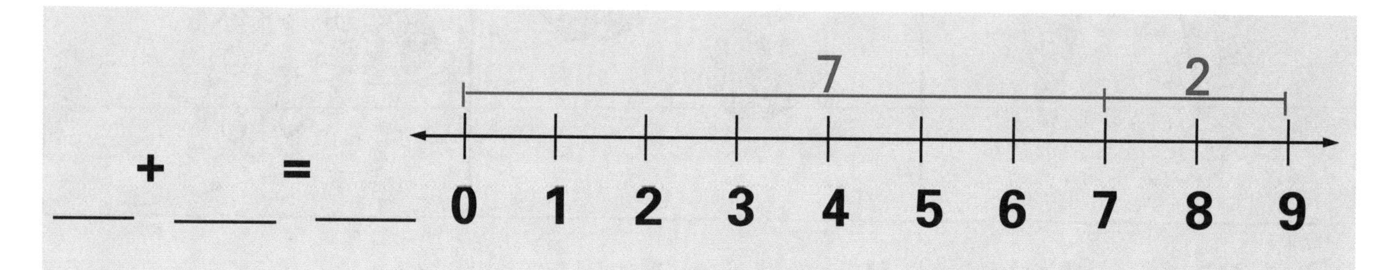

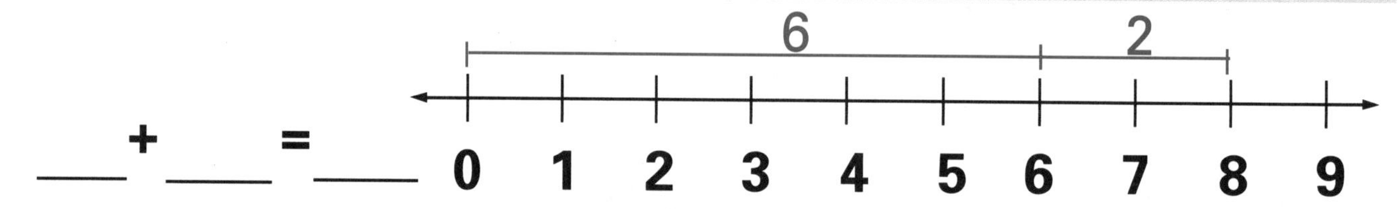

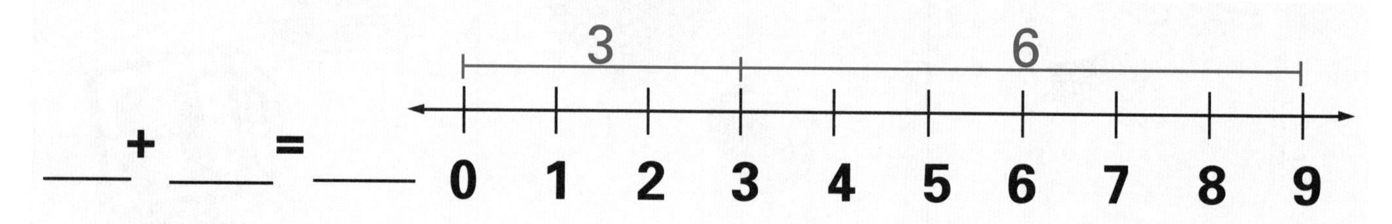

⑤ **Write < or > between each set of numbers.**

1 ___ 7	6 ___ 2	3 ___ 4
4 ___ 1	2 ___ 9	5 ___ 8
3 ___ 6	8 ___ 7	4 ___ 9

ADDITION ON THE NUMBER LINE

① **Draw the addition fact on the number line.**

2+7=9 — 0 1 2 3 4 5 6 7 8 9 (example: 2, 7)

2+0=2 — 0 1 2 3 4 5 6 7 8 9

1+8=9 — 0 1 2 3 4 5 6 7 8 9

4+5=9 — 0 1 2 3 4 5 6 7 8 9

3+4=7 — 0 1 2 3 4 5 6 7 8 9

5+1=6 — 0 1 2 3 4 5 6 7 8 9

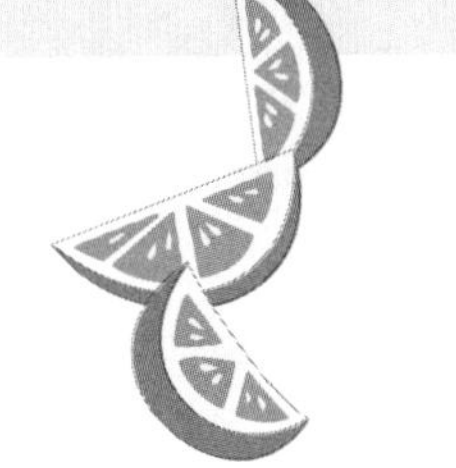

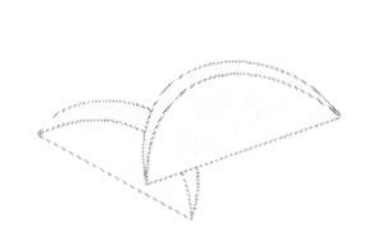

② **When counting by 2's, write the number that comes between.**

2 ___ 6   42 ___ 46   76 ___ 80

66 ___ 70   34 ___ 38   82 ___ 86

28 ___ 32   10 ___ 14   54 ___ 58

③ **Write < or > between each set of numbers. Read each set.**

16 ___ 19	23 ___ 4	35 ___ 38
19 ___ 37	21 ___ 12	41 ___ 34
28 ___ 32	32 ___ 23	42 ___ 45

④ **Write the number for the groups of ten.**

2 tens = ___	8 tens = ___	9 tens = ___
4 tens = ___	5 tens = ___	7 tens = ___
6 tens = ___	3 tens = ___	1 ten = ___

TEST 1

① **Put an X on the third tepee. Circle the seventh one. Put a box around the fifth tepee.** 3 pts.

② **Draw a set of 4 circles. Draw a set of 6 X's.** 2 pts.

③ **Count the objects in each set. Write the number in the box.** 3 pts. total for this exercise.

④ **Count the groups of ten. Count the ones. Write the number.** **6 pts. total for this exercise.**

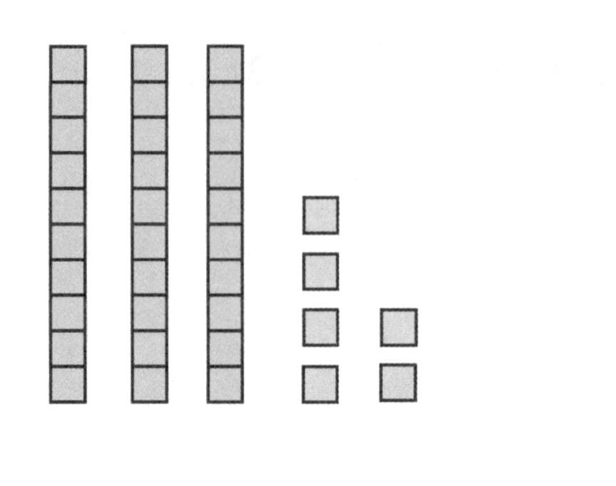

___tens ___ones

_____

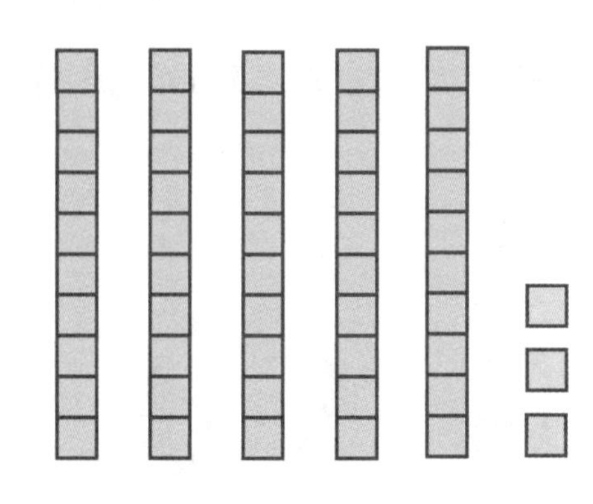

___tens ___ones

_____

⑤ **Write the answer to the addition facts shown on the number line.** **3 pts. total for this exercise.**

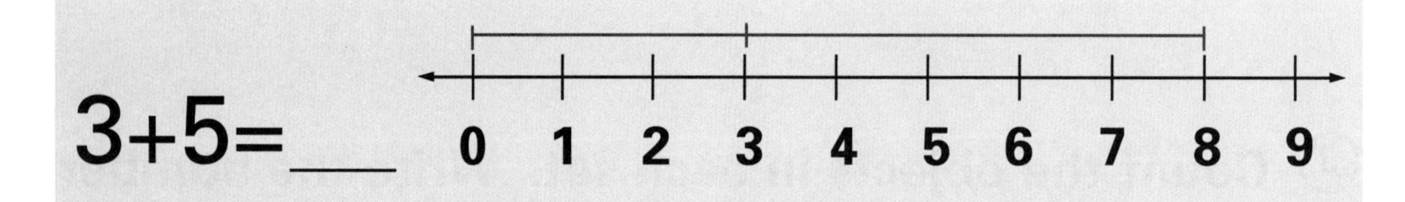

2+3=___ 0 1 2 3 4 5 6 7 8 9

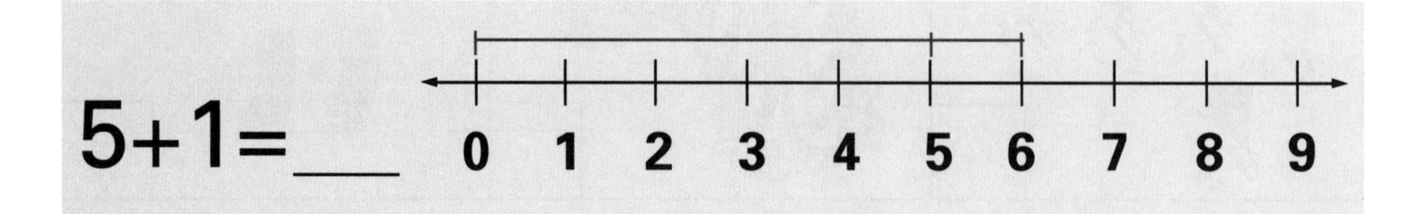

17 pts. Total

TALLY MARKS

1 Count the objects. Trace over the tally marks with your pencil.

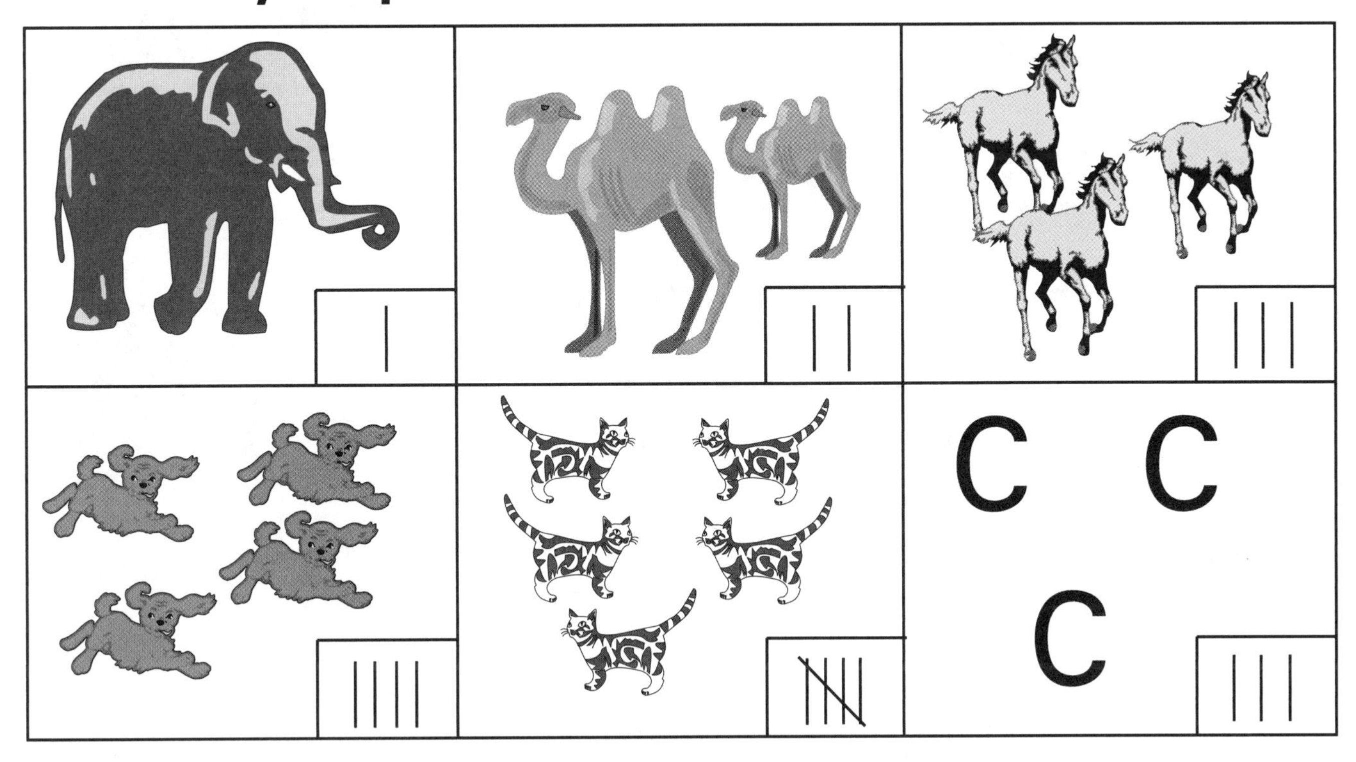

2 Make a tally mark for each object.

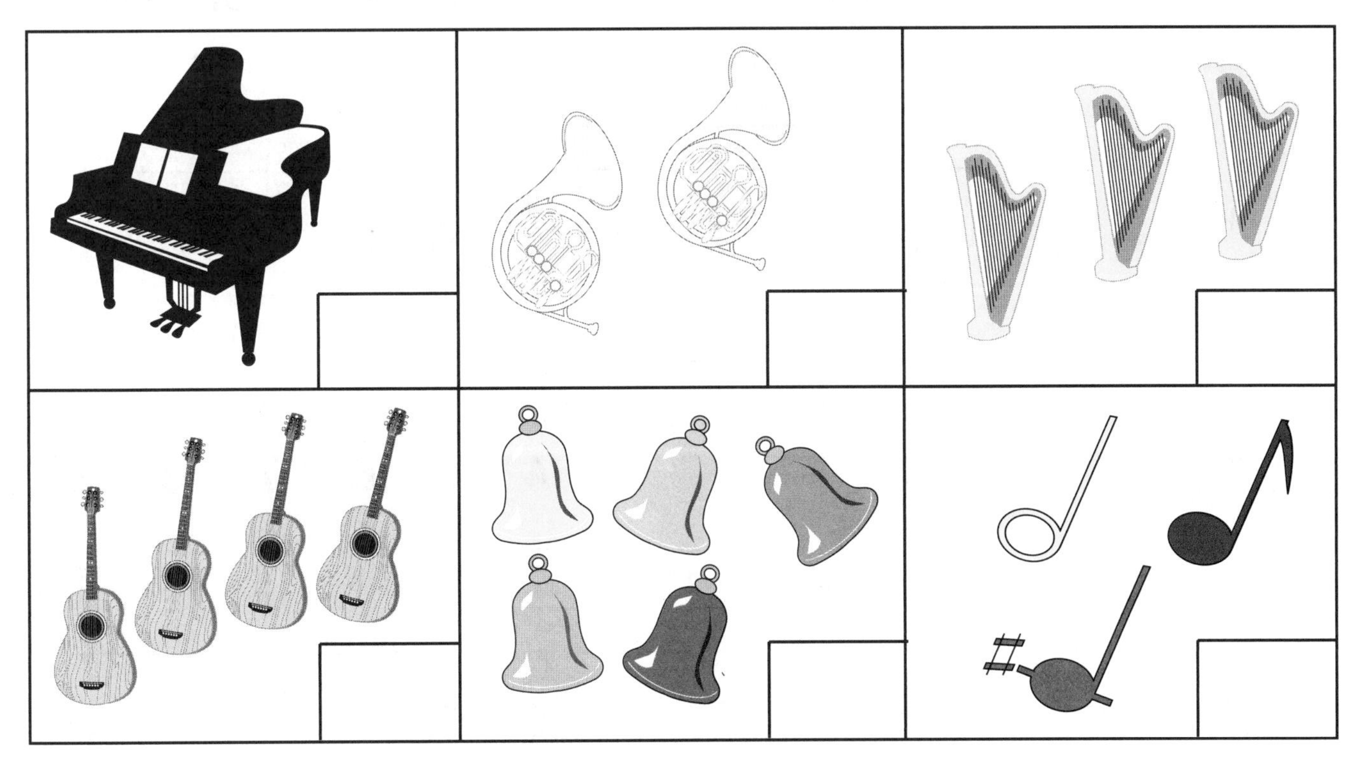

3 **Write < or > between each set of numbers. Read each set.**

8 ___ 15   25 ___ 32   34 ___ 79

29 ___ 30   16 ___ 12   49 ___ 36

4 **Write the numbers in the blanks.**

53 = ____ tens + ____ ones = 50 + 3

36 = ____ tens + ____ ones = ____ + ____

27 = ____ tens + ____ ones = ____ + ____

5 **Write the addition facts shown on the number line.**

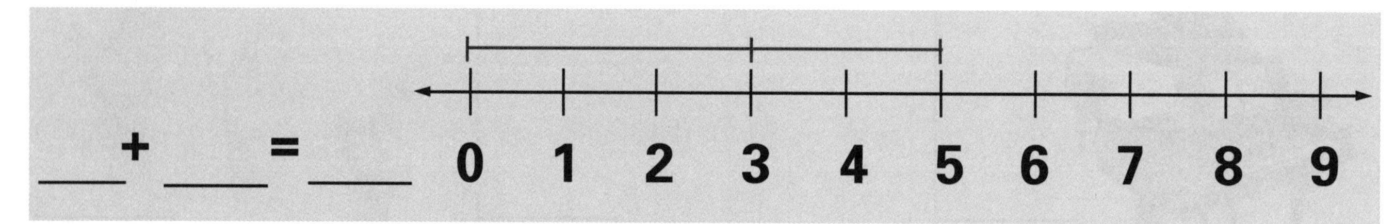

___ + ___ = ___   0 1 2 3 4 5 6 7 8 9

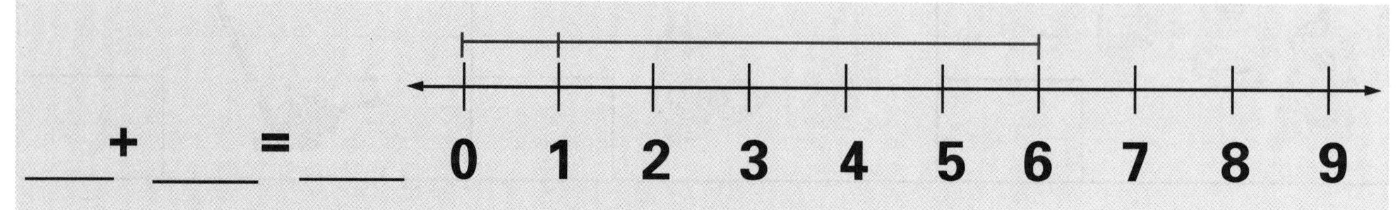

WORD NUMBERS

1 Count the objects. Draw a line to match the number of objects with the word number.

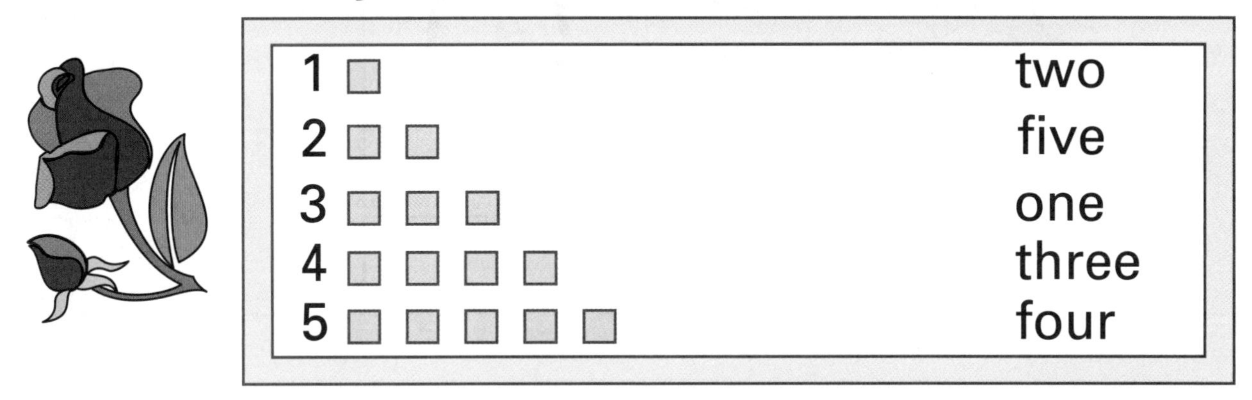

2 Write the value of the tens. Write the value of the ones.

36 = 30 + 6   96 = ___ + ___

45 = ___ + ___   23 = ___ + ___

89 = ___ + ___   11 = ___ + ___

57 = ___ + ___   78 = ___ + ___

3 When counting by 5's, write the number that comes between.

5 ___ 15   50 ___ 60   45 ___ 55

35 ___ 45   20 ___ 30   10 ___ 20

4 Make a tally mark for each object.

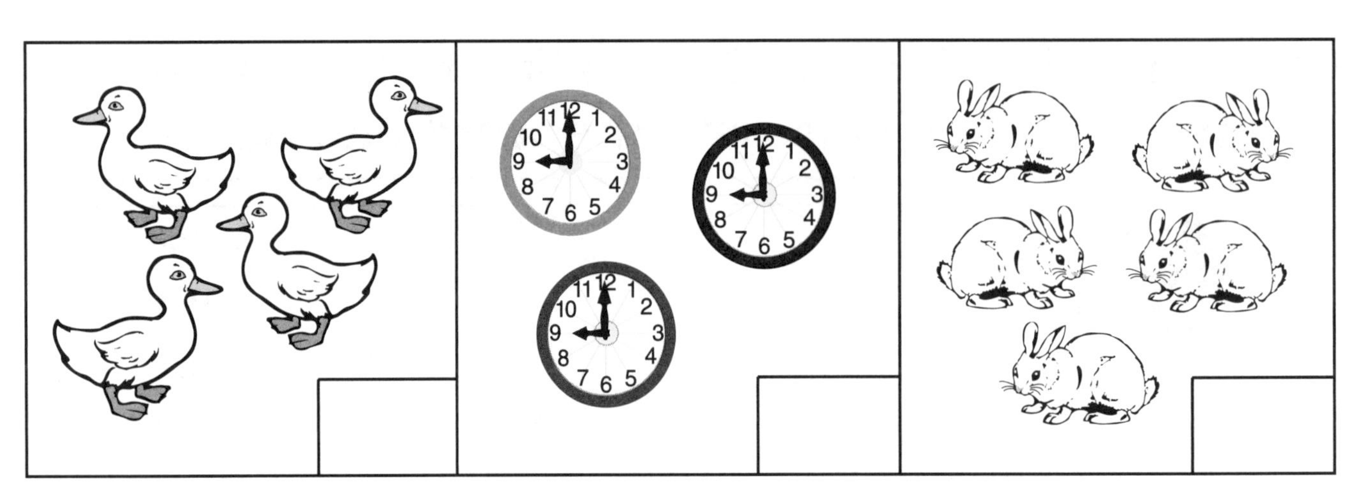

5 Write the addition facts shown on the number lines.

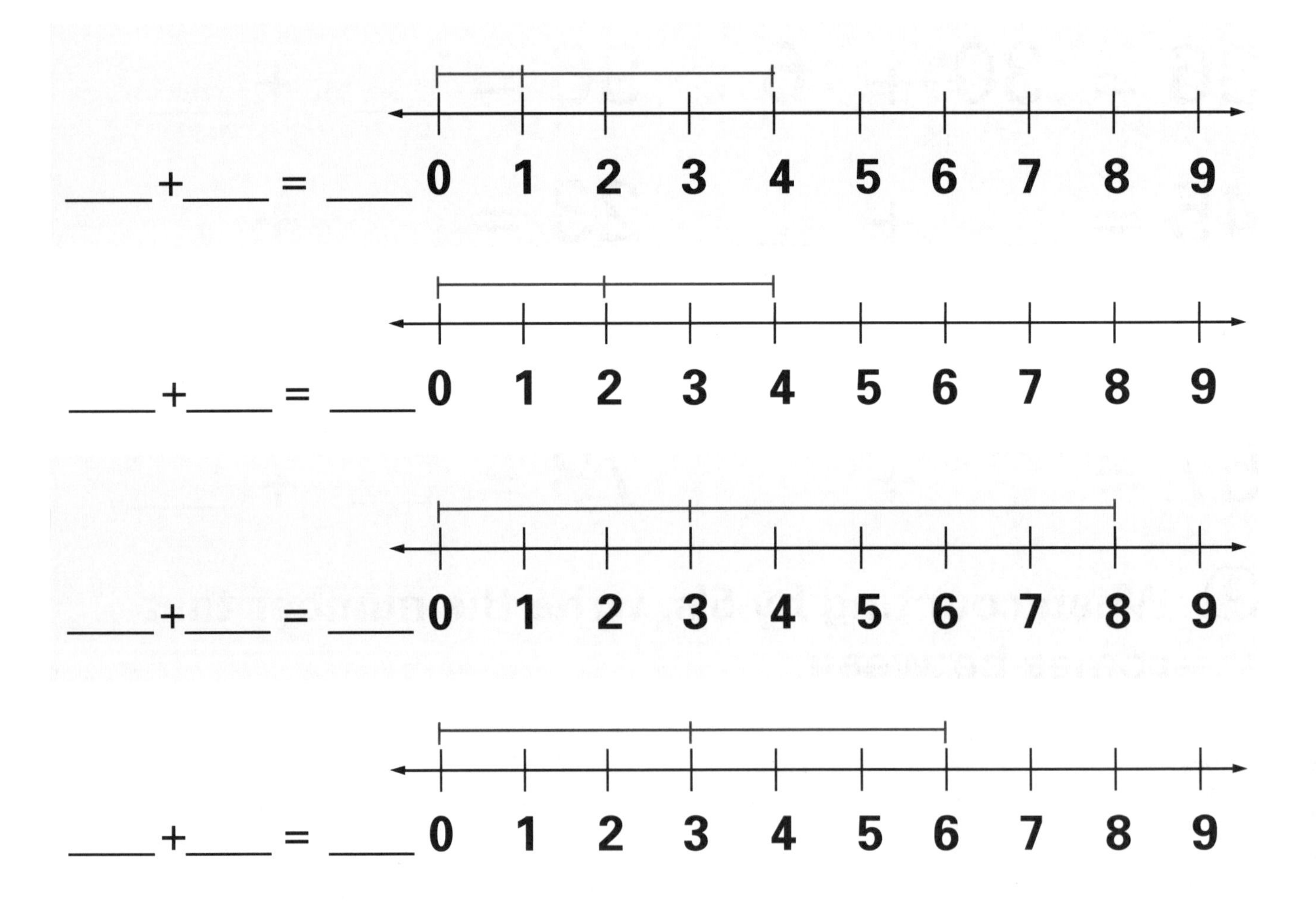

CALENDAR – MONTHS OF THE YEAR

① **Circle the first month of the year.**

May January November

Circle the last month of the year.

February August December

② **Make a tally mark for each object.**

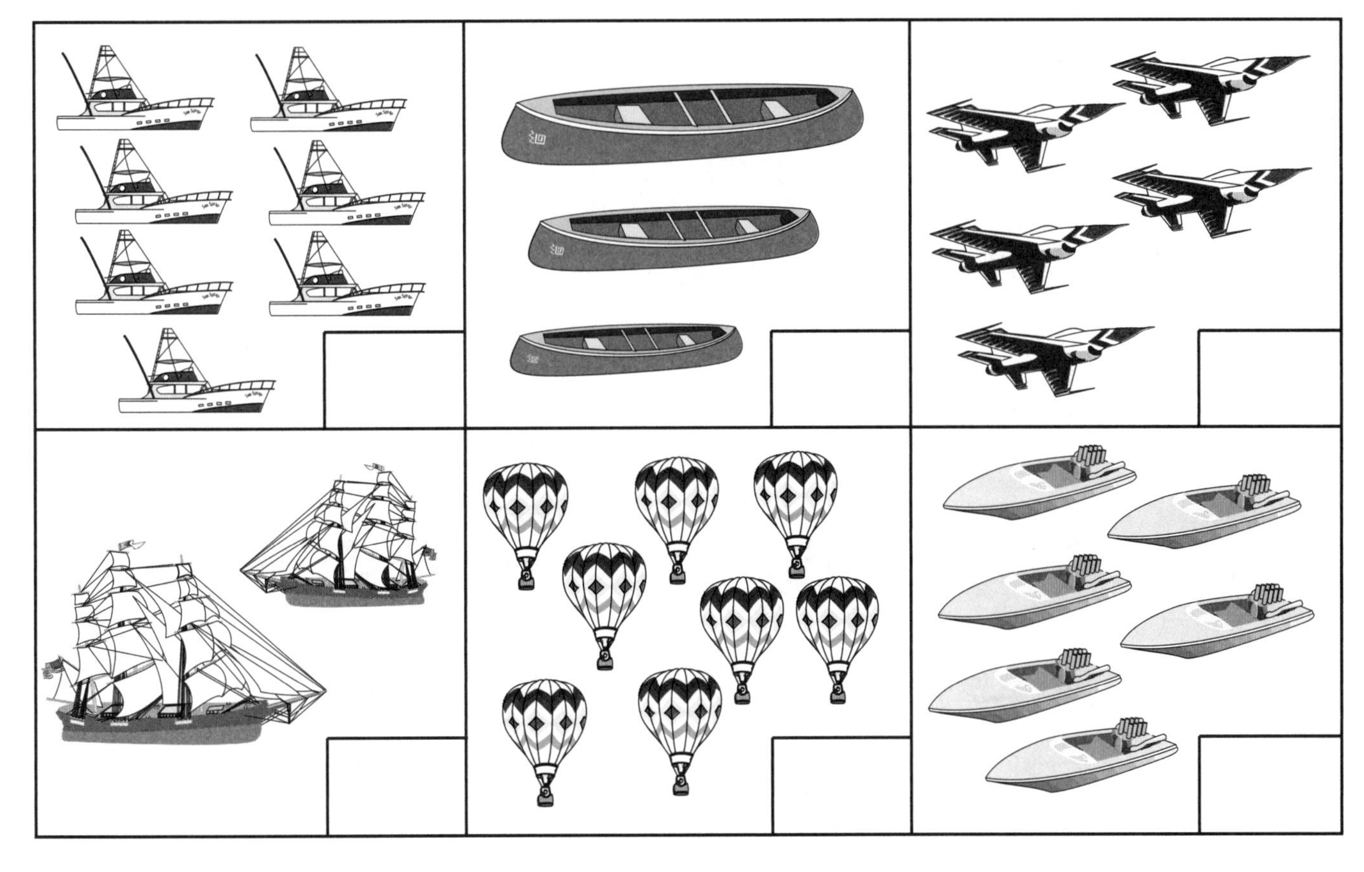

③ **Count the objects. Draw a line to match the word number with the number of objects.**

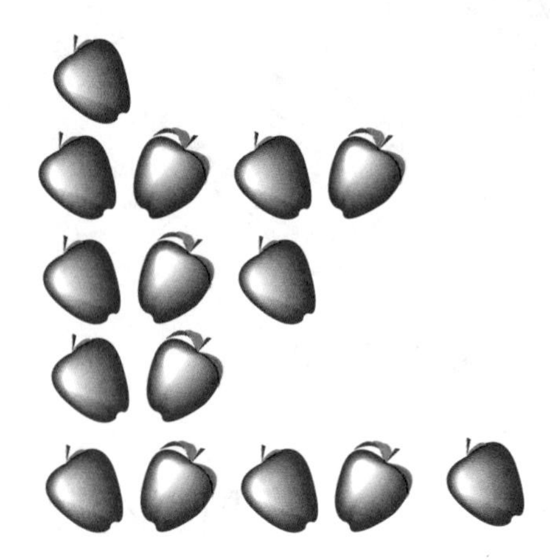

two

four

five

one

three

④ **Write the answer to each addition fact by using the number line.**

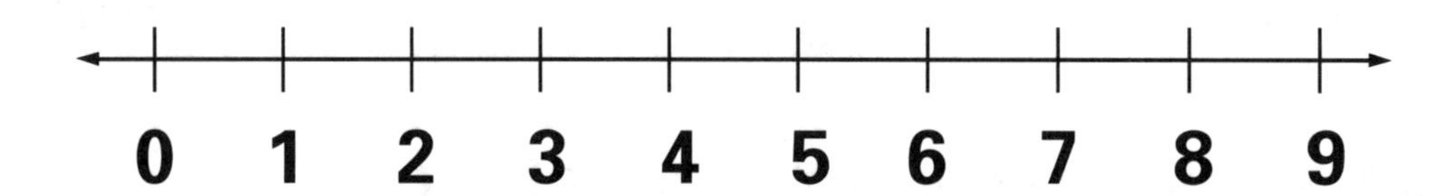

$1 + 6 =$ ___

$3 + 3 =$ ___

$2 + 3 =$ ___

$8 + 1 =$ ___

$3 + 1 =$ ___

$4 + 2 =$ ___

$6 + 3 =$ ___

$5 + 3 =$ ___

$4 + 4 =$ ___

$6 + 0 =$ ___

Lesson 13

EQUAL AND NOT EQUAL

① **Write = or ≠ between each set.**

(banana) ___ (banana)	(circle) ___ (triangle)	4 ___ 6
||| ___ ||	(tally 5) ___ (tally 5)	18 ___ 8

② **Draw a line to match the word number with the number.**

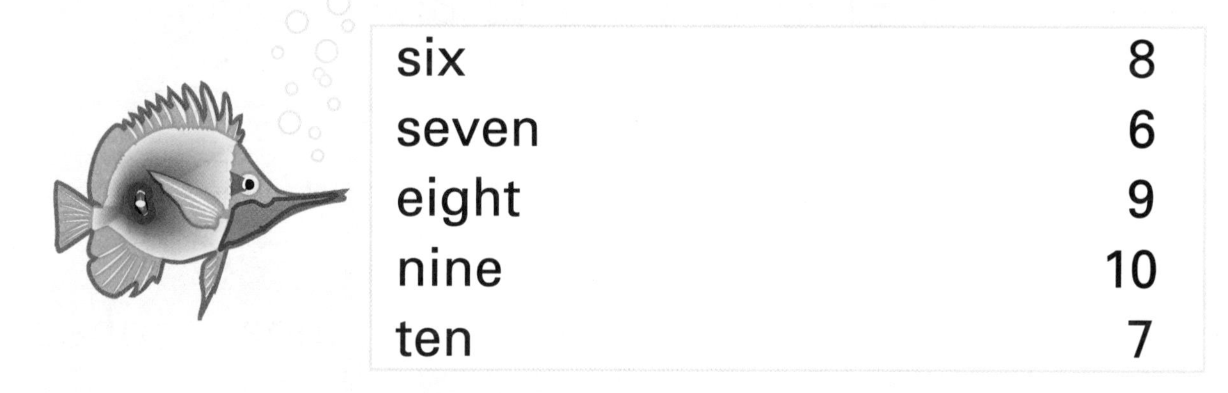

six	8
seven	6
eight	9
nine	10
ten	7

③ **When counting by tens, write the number that comes between.**

10 ___ 30   30 ___ 50   60 ___ 80

40 ___ 60   20 ___ 40   70 ___ 90

50 ___ 70   80 ___ 100

④ **Count the tens. Count the ones. Write the number.**

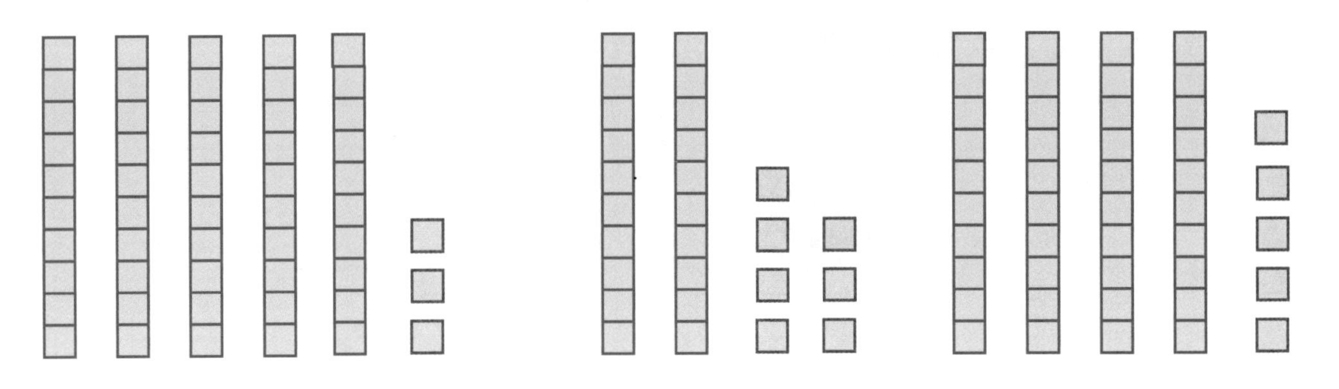

___tens ___ones ___tens ___ones ___tens ___ones

_____ _____ _____

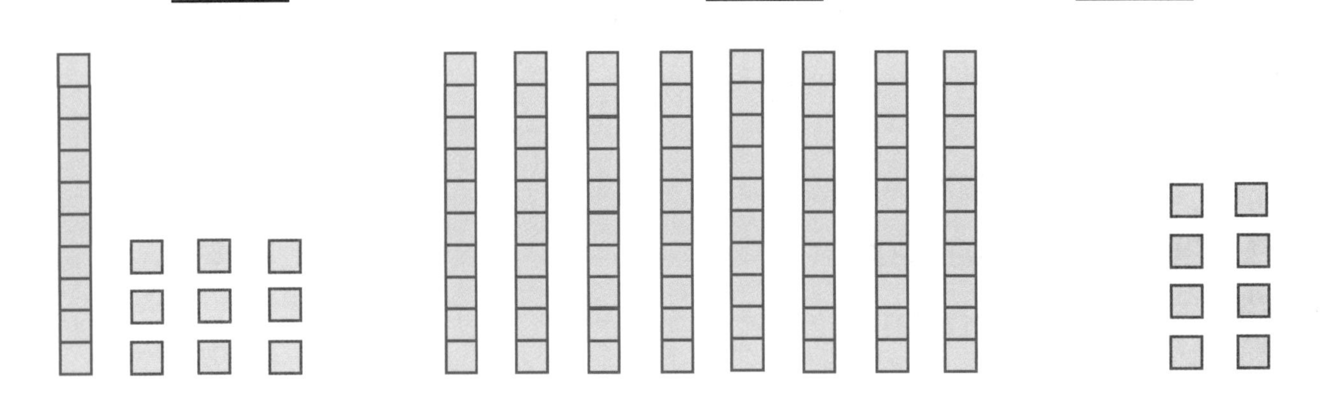

___tens ___ones ___tens ___ones ___tens ___ones

_____ _____ _____

⑤ **Write the answer to the addition facts using the number line.**

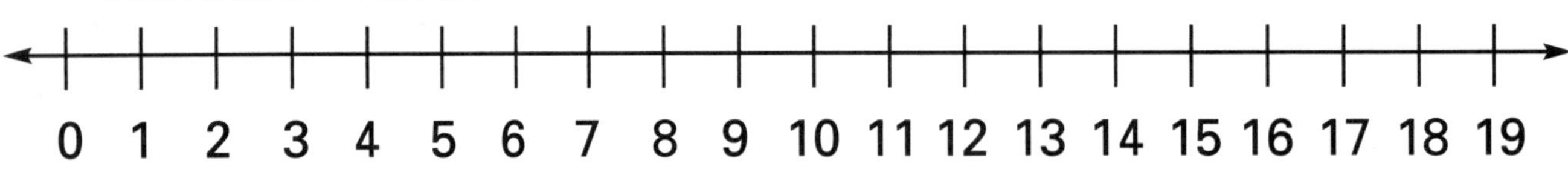

2 + 8 = ____ 5 + 8 = ____ 9 + 9 = ____

4 + 7 = ____ 9 + 6 = ____ 7 + 3 = ____

TALL AND SHORT

① **Circle the taller object.**

② **Circle the shorter object.**

③ **Make a tally mark for each object.**

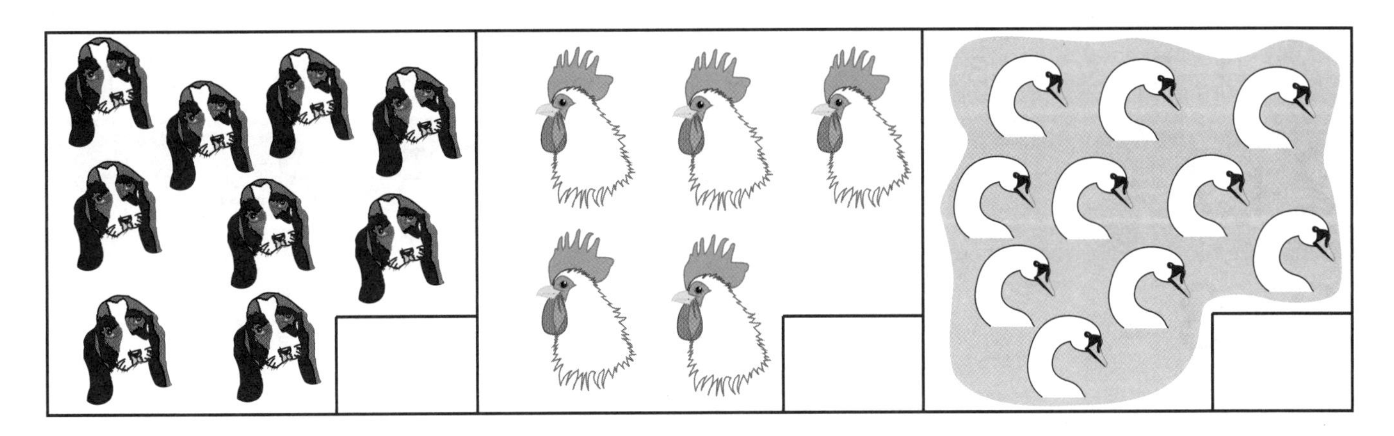

④ **Write = or ≠ between each set.**

nine ___ 𝍸|||| |||| ___ 5   six ___ 6

⑤ **Count the groups of ten by 10's. Count the ones. Write the number.**

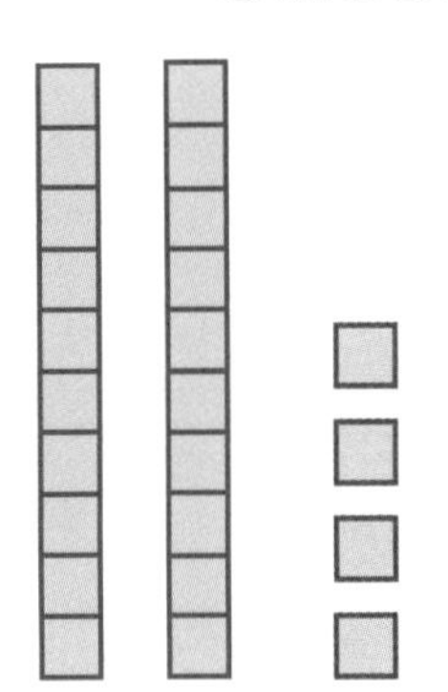

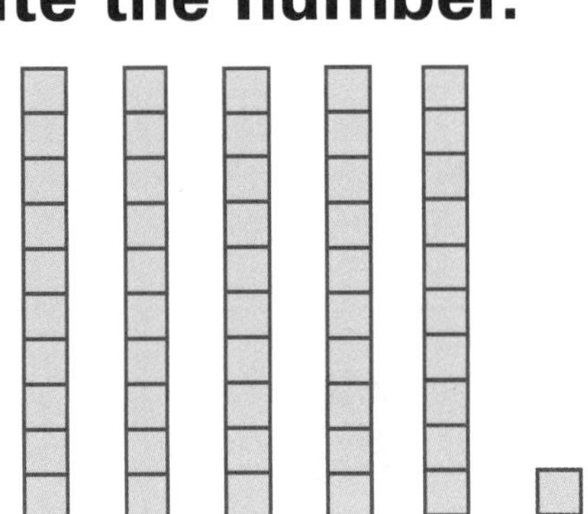

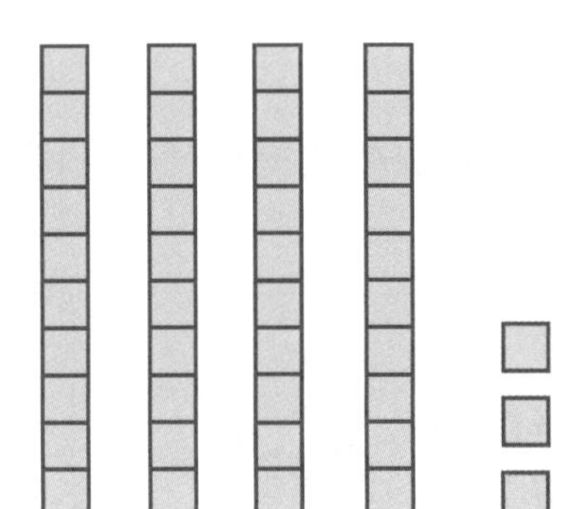

___   ___   ___

⑥ **Write the answer to the addition facts using the number line.**

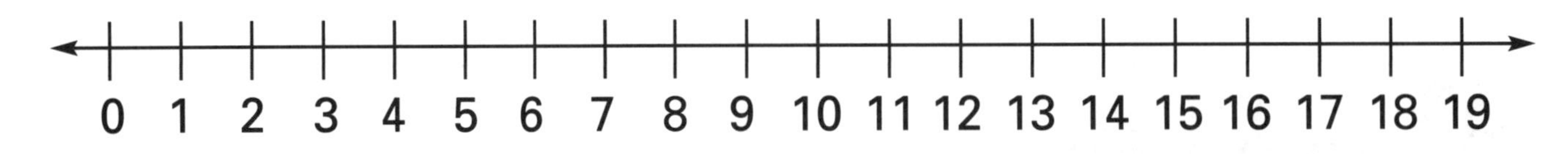

2+7= ___   5+2= ___   3+8= ___

8+3= ___   4+6= ___   6+6= ___

WORD PROBLEMS

① John has 5 balls. Sally gave him 4 more balls. How many balls does John have altogether?

John's balls + Sally's balls

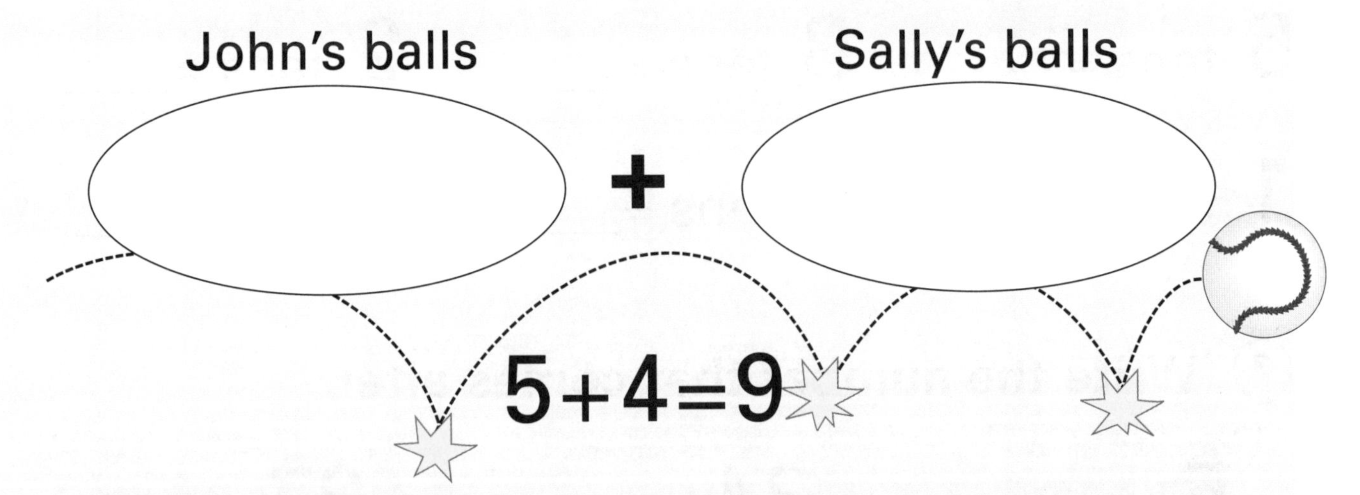

$5+4=9$

Joe has 3 pears. Dick has 5 pears. How many pears did the boys have altogether?

Joe's pears + Dick's pears

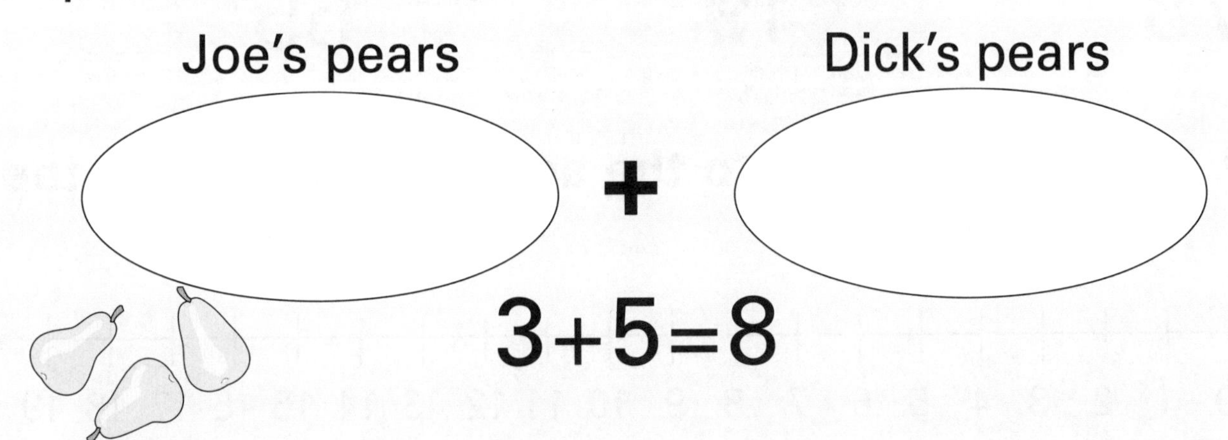

$3+5=8$

Amy had 5 hair ribbons. Mother gave her 1 more. How many hair ribbons does Amy have altogether?

Amy's ribbons + Mother's ribbons

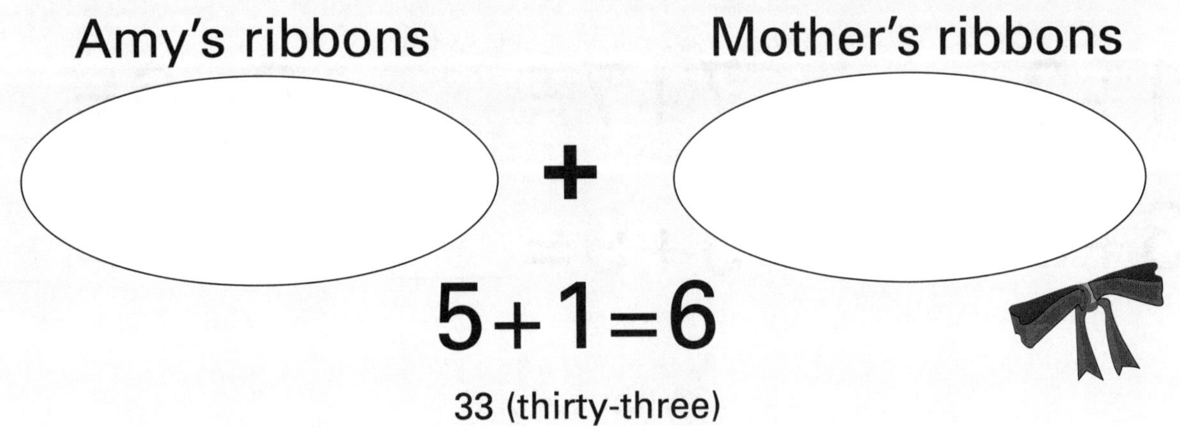

$5+1=6$

② **Write the number for the groups of ten.**

4 tens = ____ 3 tens = ____ 7 tens = ____

5 tens = ____ 8 tens = ____ 2 tens = ____

1 ten = ____ 6 tens = ____ 9 tens = ____

③ **Write the number that comes after.**

5 ___ 34 ___ 27 ___

78 ___ 19 ___ 65 ___

④ **Write the answer to the addition facts using the number line.**

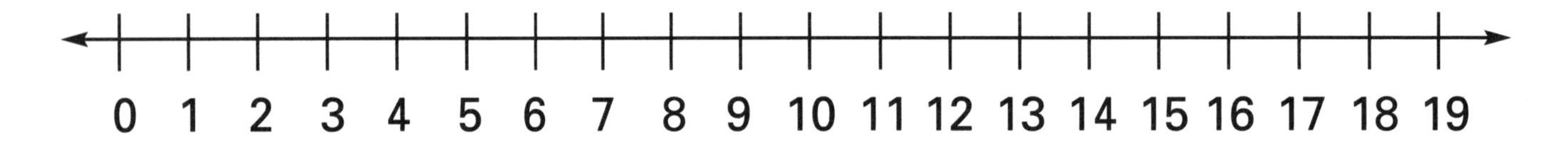

0+7= ___ 4+8= ___ 8+8= ___

1+2= ___ 7+7= ___ 9+6= ___

3+5= ___ 5+9= ___ 7+4= ___

TIME – HOUR

① **Write the correct time.** 1 hour = 60 minutes

____ o'clock ____ o'clock ____ o'clock ____ o'clock

____ o'clock ____ o'clock ____ o'clock ____ o'clock

____ o'clock ____ o'clock ____ o'clock ____ o'clock

② **Write the number that comes after.**

8 ___ 37 ___ 23 ___

75 ___ 12 ___ 69 ___

3. Susie ate 4 cookies. Mary ate 2 cookies. How many cookies did the girls eat altogether?

4. **Write the answer to the addition facts using the number line.**

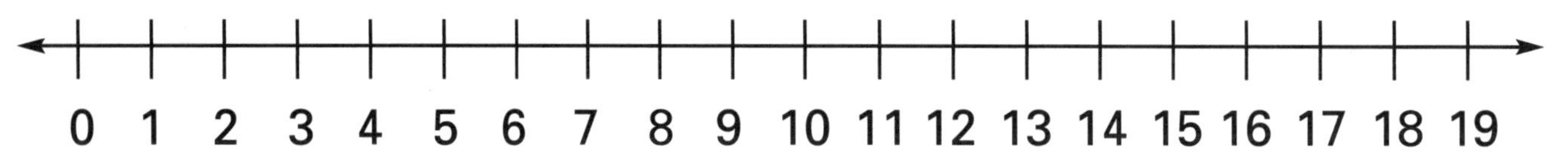

8+2= ___	7+3= ___	9+2= ___
5+5= ___	8+1= ___	7+1= ___
6+5= ___	6+4= ___	9+3= ___
7+2= ___	9+0= ___	6+7= ___
5+4= ___	8+3= ___	7+7= ___

CALENDAR – DAYS OF THE WEEK

① **Circle the second day of the week.**
Put an X on the fourth day of the week.
Put a box around the seventh day of the week.

Sunday Monday Tuesday Wednesday Thursday Friday Saturday

② **Write the numbers in the blanks.**

76 = ____ tens + ____ ones = 70 + 6

28 = ____ tens + ____ ones = ____ + ____

41 = ____ tens + ____ ones = ____ + ____

③ **Write the correct time in two ways.**

:	:	:	:
____ o'clock	____ o'clock	____ o'clock	____ o'clock

④ **Draw a line to match the number to the tally marks.**

𝍸	2
||	7
𝍸 ||	5

𝍸 𝍸	4
||||	8
𝍸 |||	10

⑤ **Write the answer to the addition facts using the number line.**

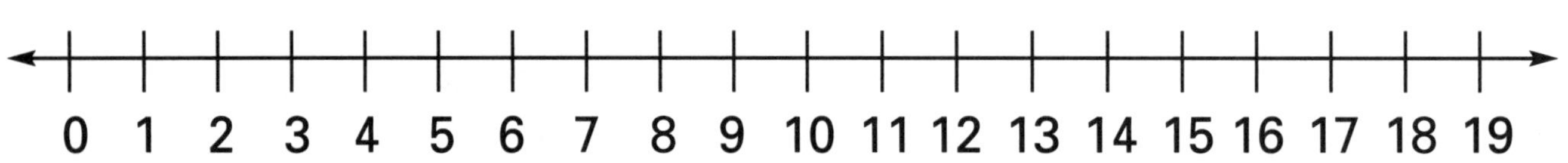

$4+7=$ ___ $3+6=$ ___ $8+9=$ ___

$6+2=$ ___ $5+4=$ ___ $3+4=$ ___

⑥ Seth made 3 baskets. His brother Joseph made 1 . How many baskets did they make altogether?

Seth's baskets Joseph's baskets

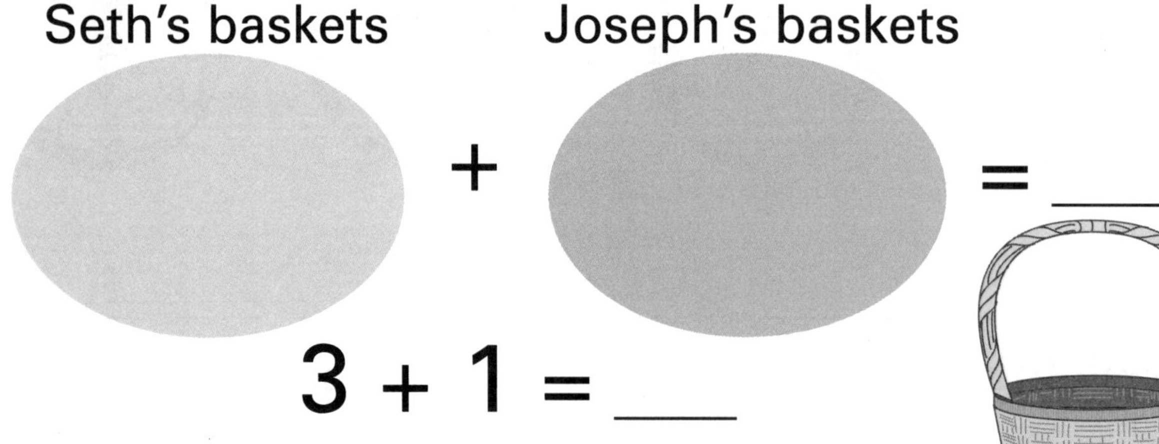

$3 + 1 =$ ___

VERTICAL ADDITION

① **Write the answers.**

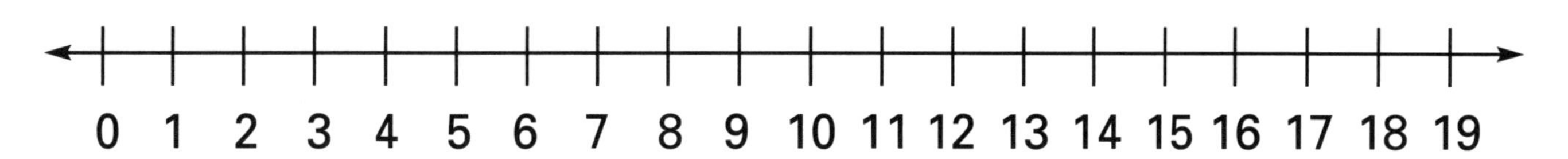

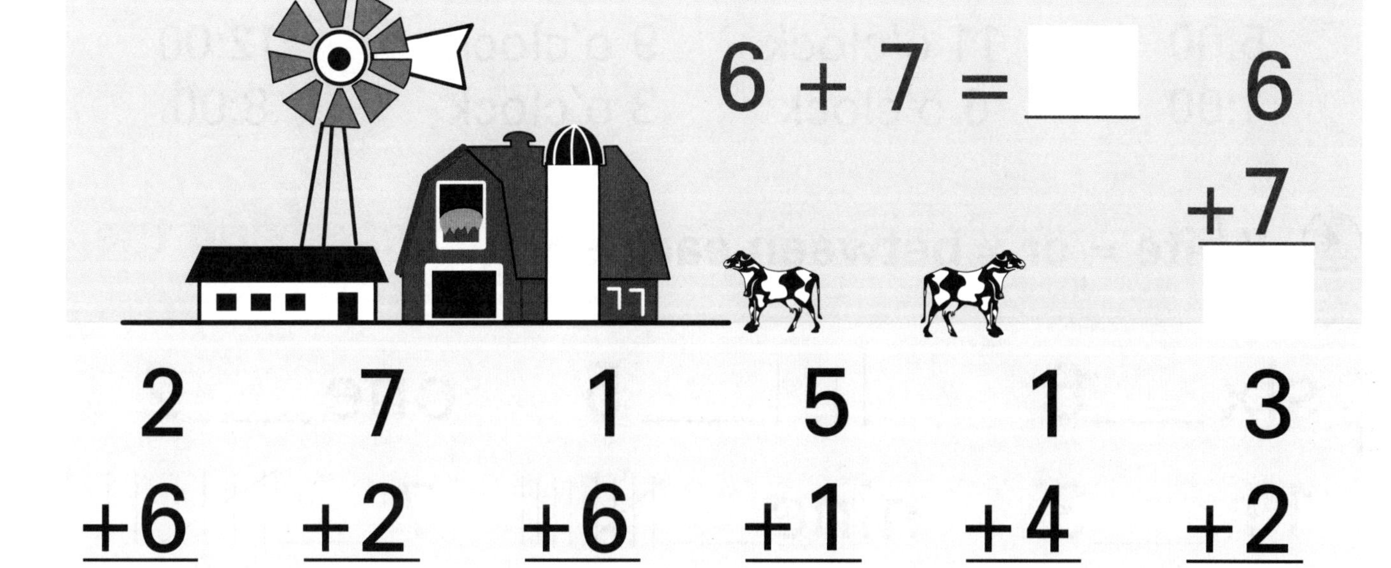

6 + 7 = ___

$$\begin{array}{r} 6 \\ +7 \\ \hline \end{array}$$

$$\begin{array}{r} 2 \\ +6 \\ \hline \end{array} \quad \begin{array}{r} 7 \\ +2 \\ \hline \end{array} \quad \begin{array}{r} 1 \\ +6 \\ \hline \end{array} \quad \begin{array}{r} 5 \\ +1 \\ \hline \end{array} \quad \begin{array}{r} 1 \\ +4 \\ \hline \end{array} \quad \begin{array}{r} 3 \\ +2 \\ \hline \end{array}$$

$$\begin{array}{r} 6 \\ +3 \\ \hline \end{array} \quad \begin{array}{r} 5 \\ +3 \\ \hline \end{array} \quad \begin{array}{r} 4 \\ +2 \\ \hline \end{array} \quad \begin{array}{r} 5 \\ +4 \\ \hline \end{array} \quad \begin{array}{r} 3 \\ +5 \\ \hline \end{array} \quad \begin{array}{r} 5 \\ +2 \\ \hline \end{array}$$

② **Counting by 2's, write the number that comes after.**

8 ___ 14 ___ 26 ___

30 ___ 42 ___ 54 ___

68 ___ 70 ___ 86 ___

③ Circle the correct time.

5:00	11 o'clock	9 o'clock	12:00
1:00	6 o'clock	3 o'clock	8:00

④ Write = or ≠ between each set.

six ___ 6	|||| ___ 5	one ___ 2
11 ___ 3	nine ___ ~~||||~~ ||||	7 ___ ~~||||~~ ||
eight ___ ~~||||~~ |||	four ___ 4	five ___ ~~||||~~ |

⑤ Bill counted four cows by the fence. Jonathan counted three more by the barn. How many cows were there altogether?

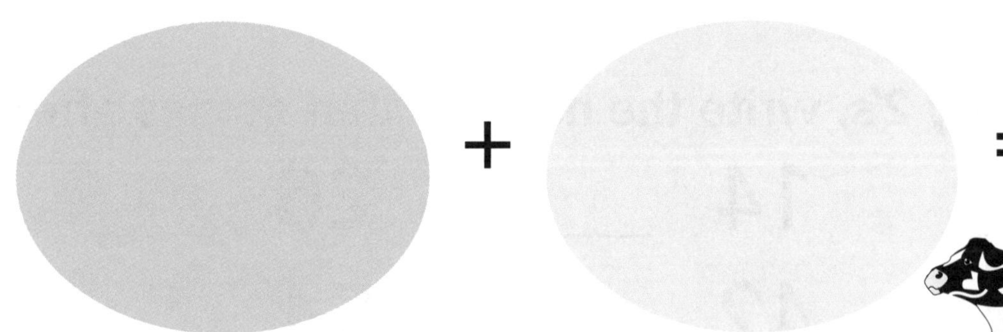

+ = ___

$4 + 3 =$ ___

ADDITION – OPPOSITES

① **Add.**

3	6	5	4	2	3
+6	+3	+4	+5	+3	+2

7	3	1	2	5	9
+3	+7	+2	+1	+9	+5

8	7	2	5	6	9
+7	+8	+5	+2	+9	+6

② **Counting by 2's, write the number that comes after.**

94 ___ 32 ___ 58 ___

70 ___ 46 ___ 4 ___

12 ___ 28 ___

③ Draw a line to match the time to the clock.

4:00   9 o'clock   12:00   1 o'clock

④ Paul has 7 marbles in his pocket. James gave him 2 more marbles. How many marbles do Paul and James have altogether? ____ + ____ = ____

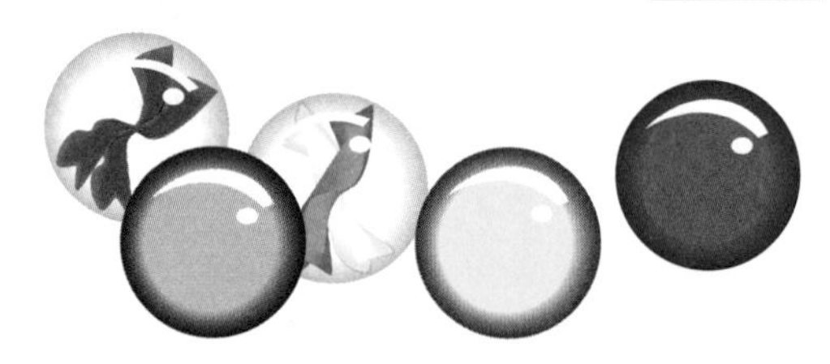

⑤ Write the answers.

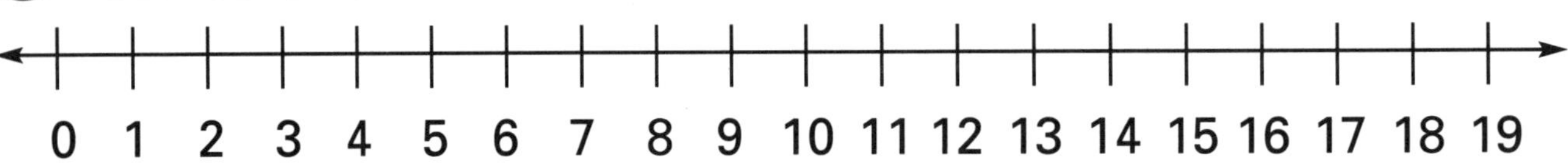

2	3	3	1	2	4
+3	+5	+4	+2	+4	+4

2	8	7	4	5	9
+7	+4	+7	+5	+6	+6

TEST 2

① **Count the groups of tens by 10's. Count the ones. Write the number.** **3 pts. total for this exercise.**

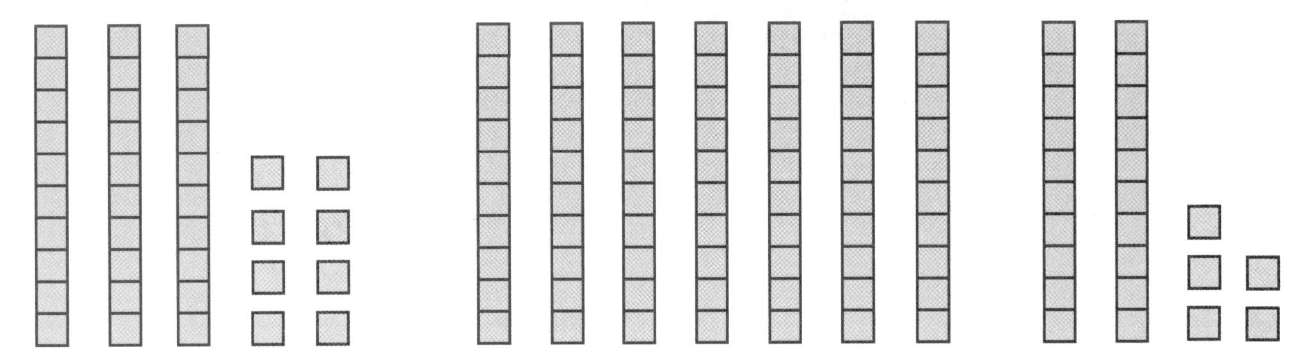

____ ____ ____

② **Write the numbers in the blanks.** **10 pts.**

18 = ____ tens + ____ ones = 10 + 8

42 = ____ tens + ____ ones = ____ + ____

69 = ____ tens + ____ ones = ____ + ____

③ **Make a tally mark for each object.** **3 pts.**

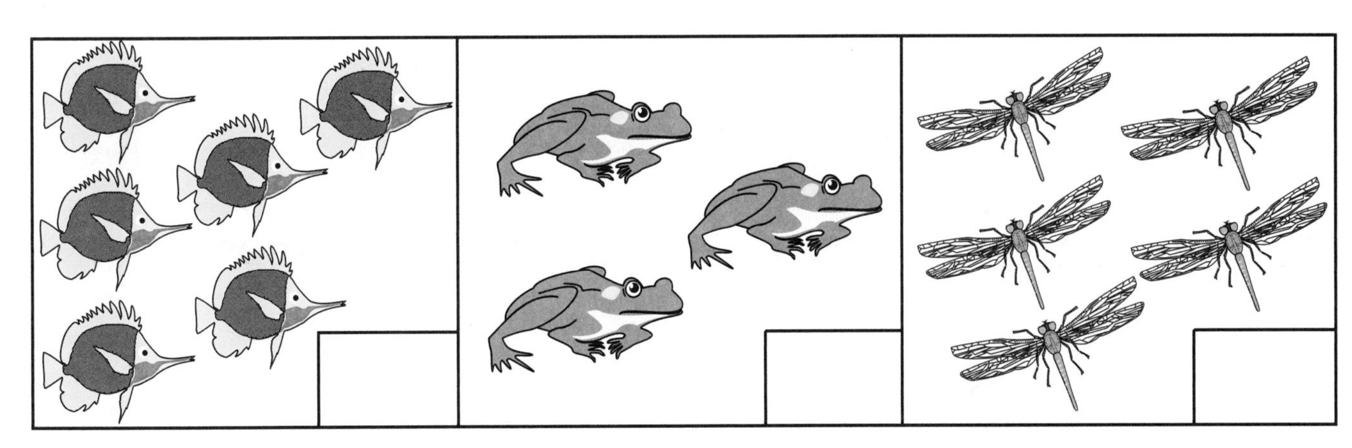

④ Draw a line to match the word number and number.
8 pts. total for this exercise.

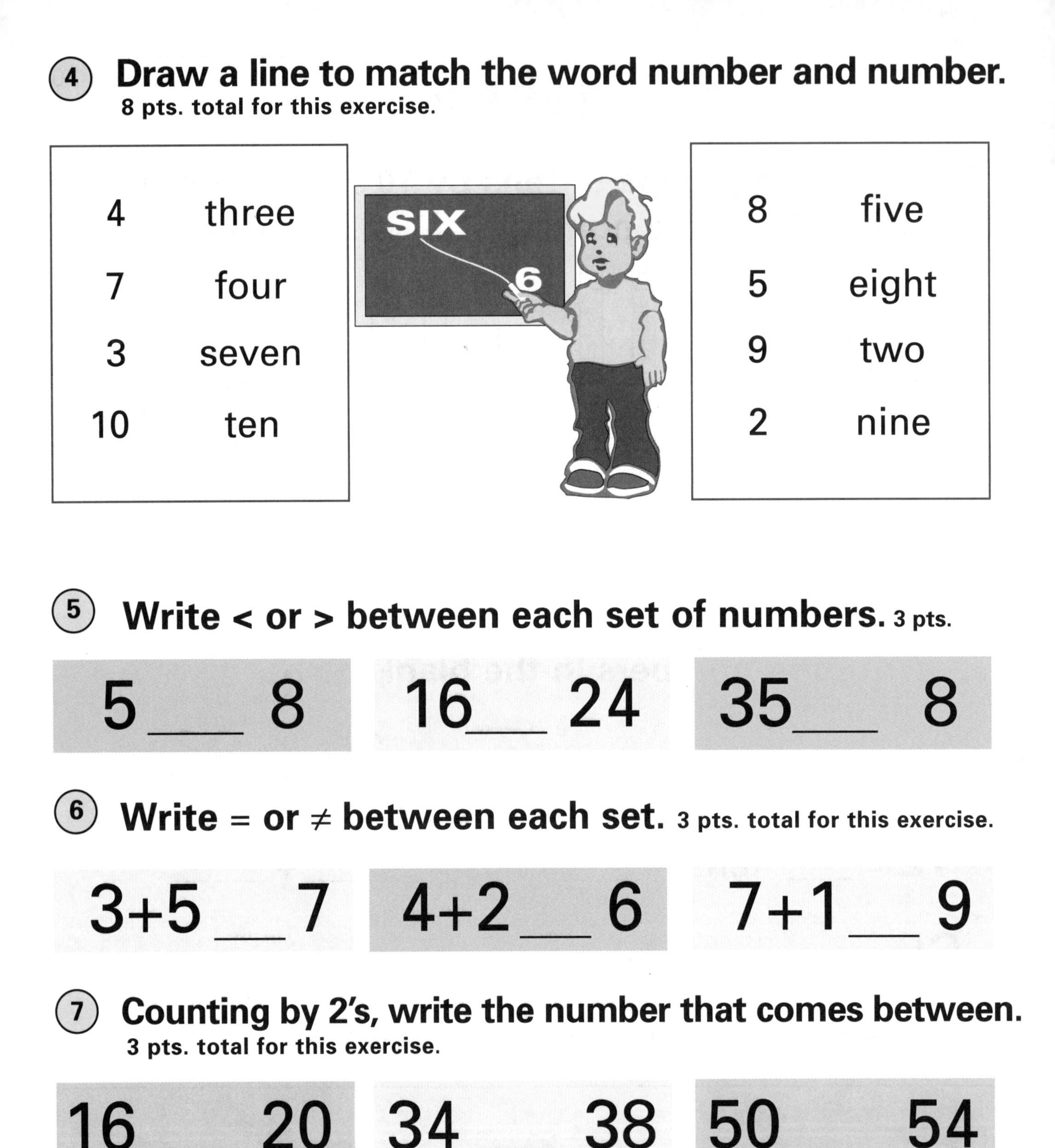

4	three
7	four
3	seven
10	ten

8	five
5	eight
9	two
2	nine

⑤ Write < or > between each set of numbers. 3 pts.

5 ___ 8 16 ___ 24 35 ___ 8

⑥ Write = or ≠ between each set. 3 pts. total for this exercise.

3+5 ___ 7 4+2 ___ 6 7+1 ___ 9

⑦ Counting by 2's, write the number that comes between.
3 pts. total for this exercise.

16 ___ 20 34 ___ 38 50 ___ 54

⑧ Counting by 5's, write the number that comes between.
3 pts. total for this exercise.

15 ___ 25 40 ___ 50 75 ___ 85

36 pts. Total

LONG AND SHORT

① Circle the longer object.

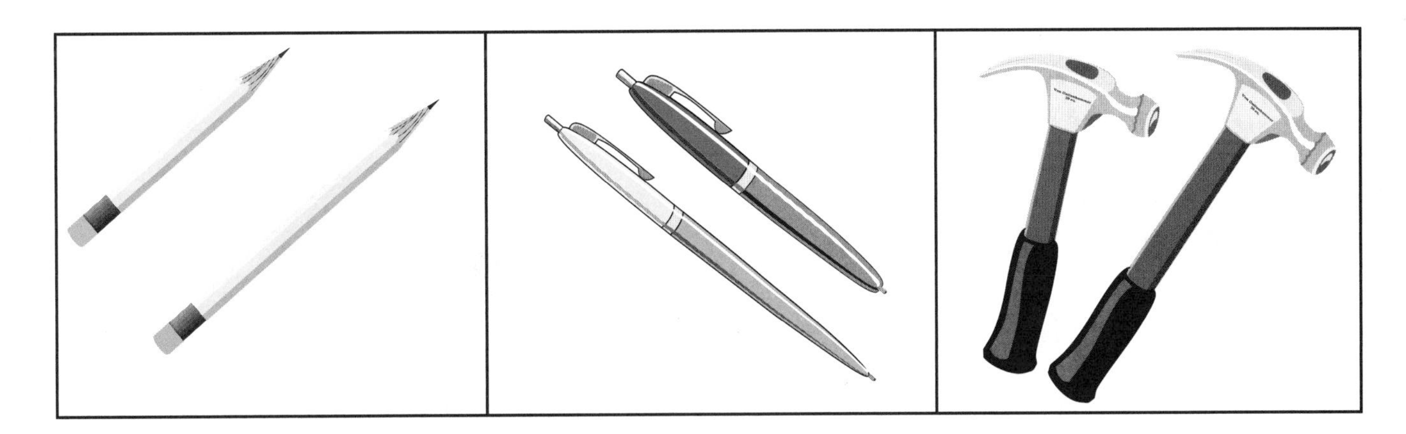

② Circle the shorter object.

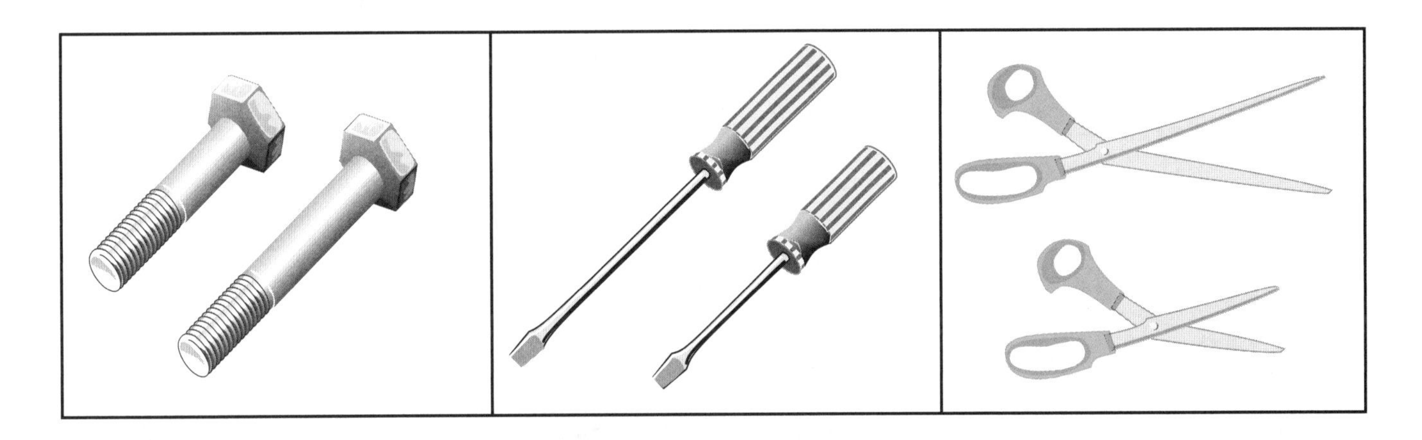

③ Draw the short hand for each clock.

④ **Write < or > between each set. Read the set.**

16 ___ 7　　38 ___ 42　　57 ___ 50

86 ___ 79　　24 ___ 27　　60 ___ 65

⑤ **Write the answers.**

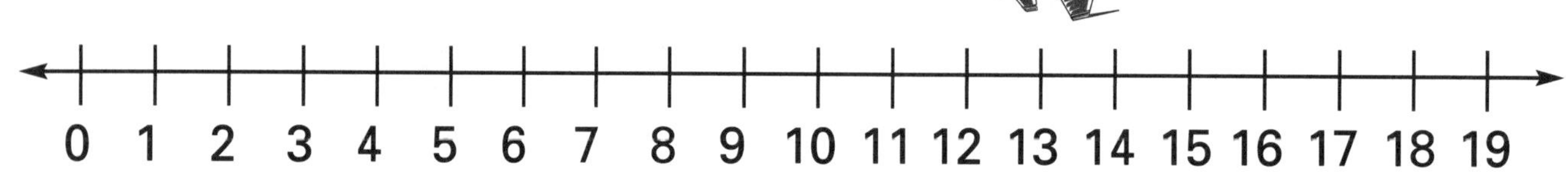

$\begin{array}{r} 5 \\ +2 \\ \hline \end{array}$	$\begin{array}{r} 3 \\ +3 \\ \hline \end{array}$	$\begin{array}{r} 4 \\ +1 \\ \hline \end{array}$	$\begin{array}{r} 2 \\ +2 \\ \hline \end{array}$	$\begin{array}{r} 5 \\ +4 \\ \hline \end{array}$	$\begin{array}{r} 2 \\ +3 \\ \hline \end{array}$
$\begin{array}{r} 3 \\ +5 \\ \hline \end{array}$	$\begin{array}{r} 3 \\ +4 \\ \hline \end{array}$	$\begin{array}{r} 1 \\ +2 \\ \hline \end{array}$	$\begin{array}{r} 2 \\ +6 \\ \hline \end{array}$	$\begin{array}{r} 6 \\ +8 \\ \hline \end{array}$	$\begin{array}{r} 7 \\ +4 \\ \hline \end{array}$
$\begin{array}{r} 8 \\ +3 \\ \hline \end{array}$	$\begin{array}{r} 7 \\ +5 \\ \hline \end{array}$	$\begin{array}{r} 6 \\ +5 \\ \hline \end{array}$	$\begin{array}{r} 9 \\ +7 \\ \hline \end{array}$	$\begin{array}{r} 3 \\ +9 \\ \hline \end{array}$	$\begin{array}{r} 9 \\ +2 \\ \hline \end{array}$

NUMBER ORDER – AFTER BY 5'S

① Counting by 5's, write the number that comes after.

5 ___ 20 ___ 35 ___ 50 ___

65 ___ 80 ___ 95 ___ 15 ___

② Write the correct time.

___ o'clock ___ o'clock ___ o'clock ___ o'clock

___:00 ___:00 ___:00 ___:00

___ o'clock ___ o'clock ___ o'clock ___ o'clock

③ Write < or > between each set. Read the set.

7 ___ 2   18 ___ 20   26 ___ 25

32 ___ 33   45 ___ 46   51 ___ 50

④ Write the answers.

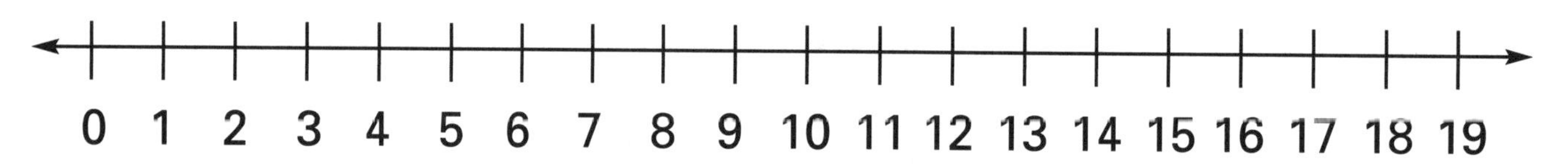

0	1	6	3	4	5
+8	+8	+2	+8	+9	+7

3	6	5	2	9	7
+2	+9	+0	+5	+1	+2

6	8	7	9	8	3
+3	+1	+8	+6	+5	+7

WORD PROBLEMS

1 Jane has 3 bunnies. Ann has 6 bunnies. How many bunnies do they have altogether?

Jane's  Ann's 

\+ = ____

____ + ____ = ____

Joan has 5 pencils. Jill has 2 pencils. How many do they have altogether?

____ + ____ = ____

Mike has 4 cars. Peter gave Mike 1 more . How many cars does Mike have altogether?

____ + ____ = ____

2 **Counting by 5's, write the number that comes after.**

25 ___	90 ___	55 ___	60 ___
10 ___	85 ___	20 ___	45 ___

3. **Counting by 6's, write the missing numbers.**

6 12 ___ ___ 30 ___ 42

48 ___ ___ 66 ___ 78 ___

4. **Draw a line to match the number and the tally marks.**

|||	3
𝍸	10
𝍸 𝍸	5

𝍸|||	7
||||	8
𝍸||	4

5. **Write the answers.**

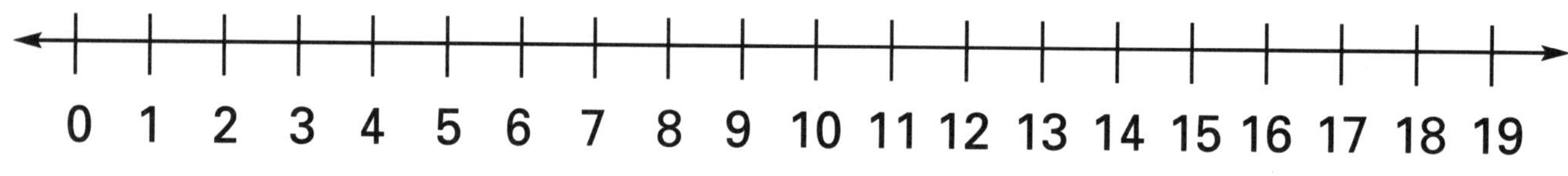

$$\begin{array}{r} 4 \\ +4 \\ \hline \end{array} \quad \begin{array}{r} 2 \\ +8 \\ \hline \end{array} \quad \begin{array}{r} 0 \\ +9 \\ \hline \end{array} \quad \begin{array}{r} 4 \\ +6 \\ \hline \end{array} \quad \begin{array}{r} 2 \\ +1 \\ \hline \end{array} \quad \begin{array}{r} 5 \\ +8 \\ \hline \end{array}$$

$$\begin{array}{r} 7 \\ +6 \\ \hline \end{array} \quad \begin{array}{r} 1 \\ +6 \\ \hline \end{array} \quad \begin{array}{r} 9 \\ +9 \\ \hline \end{array} \quad \begin{array}{r} 8 \\ +6 \\ \hline \end{array}$$

WORD PROBLEMS

① Joe found 3 pennies on the floor. Ruth found 3 pennies on her desk. How many pennies did they find altogether?

____ + ____ = ____

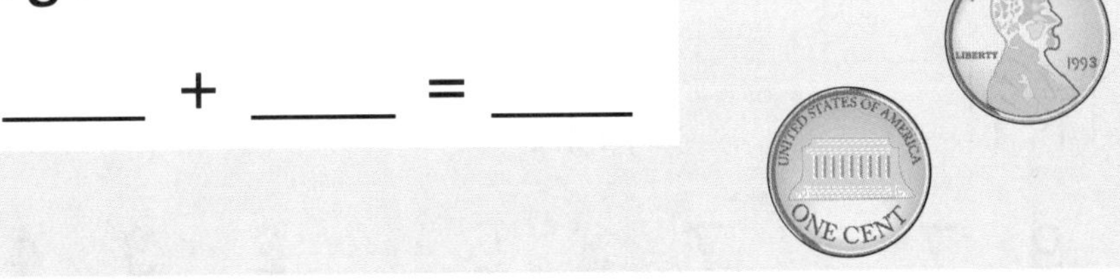

Sherry did 2 pages of math. Kay did 6 pages of math. How many pages of math did the girls do altogether?

____ + ____ = ____

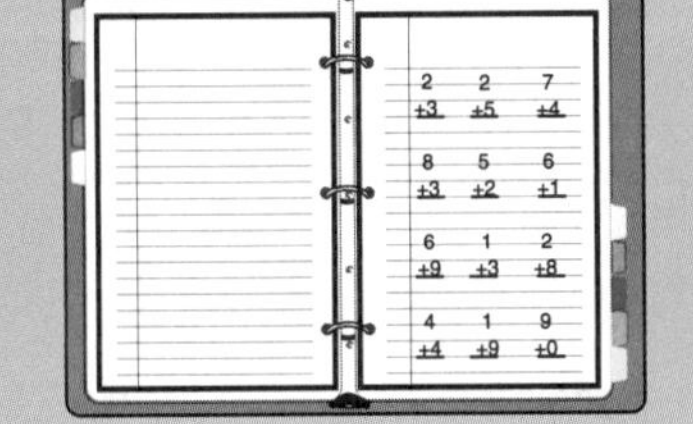

Johnny had 3 cowboy hats. Jay gave Johnny 2 more cowboy hats. How many cowboy hats did Johnny have altogether?

____ + ____ = ____

② **Write < or > between each set. Read the set.**

55 ____ 57	23 ____ 21	66 ____ 64
18 ____ 16	72 ____ 74	99 ____ 97

3 **Circle the correct number to match the tally marks.**

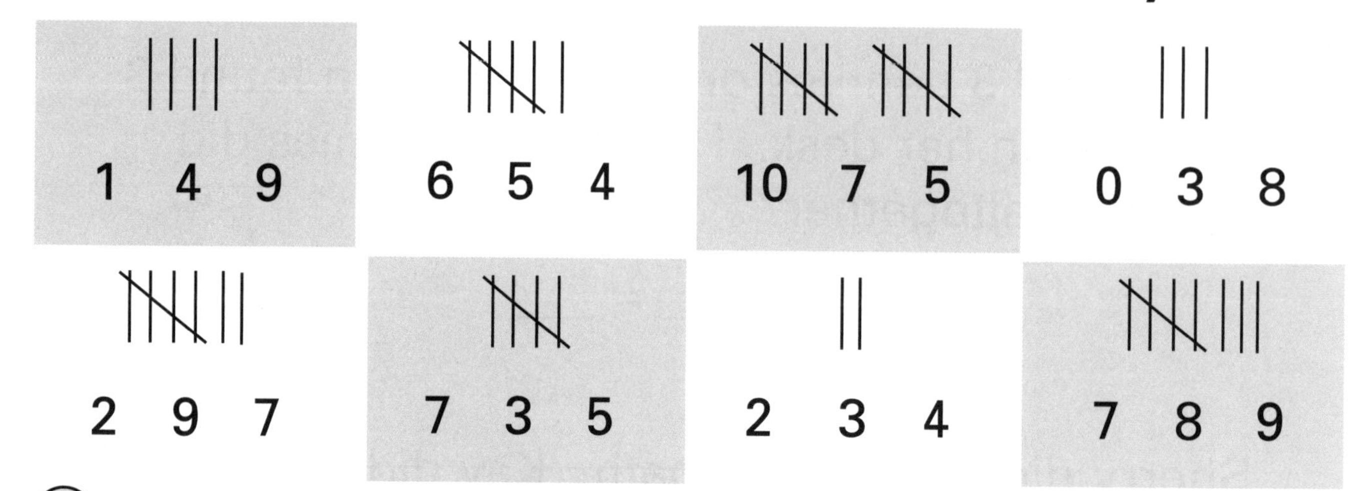

4 **Write the answers.**

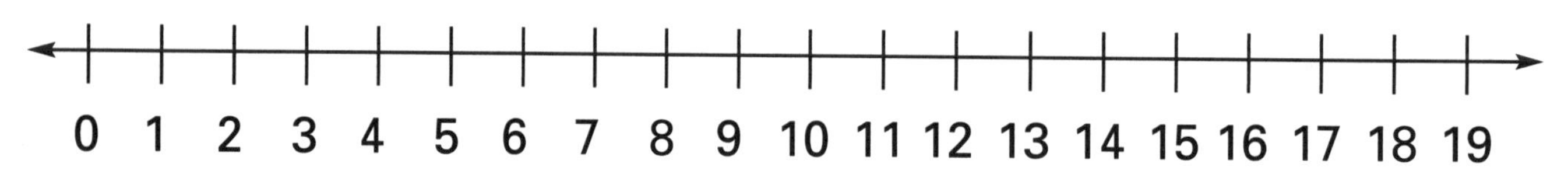

$\begin{array}{r} 2 \\ +7 \\ \hline \end{array}$ $\begin{array}{r} 9 \\ +5 \\ \hline \end{array}$ $\begin{array}{r} 0 \\ +4 \\ \hline \end{array}$ $\begin{array}{r} 4 \\ +9 \\ \hline \end{array}$ $\begin{array}{r} 4 \\ +4 \\ \hline \end{array}$ $\begin{array}{r} 3 \\ +5 \\ \hline \end{array}$

$\begin{array}{r} 7 \\ +7 \\ \hline \end{array}$ $\begin{array}{r} 6 \\ +8 \\ \hline \end{array}$ $\begin{array}{r} 3 \\ +3 \\ \hline \end{array}$ $\begin{array}{r} 7 \\ +2 \\ \hline \end{array}$ $\begin{array}{r} 8 \\ +8 \\ \hline \end{array}$ $\begin{array}{r} 8 \\ +0 \\ \hline \end{array}$

NUMBER ORDER – AFTER BY 10'S

① **Counting by 10's, write the number that comes after.**

10 ___	40 ___	70 ___	20 ___
30 ___	60 ___	50 ___	90 ___

② **Draw a line to match.**

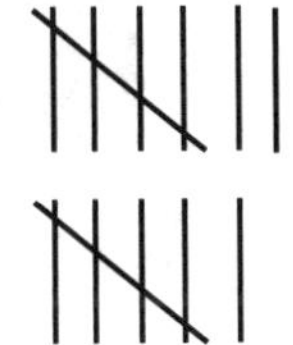

one	||	six	卌 ||
two	|||	seven	卌 |
three	|	eight	10
four	卌	nine	卌 ||||
five	4	ten	9

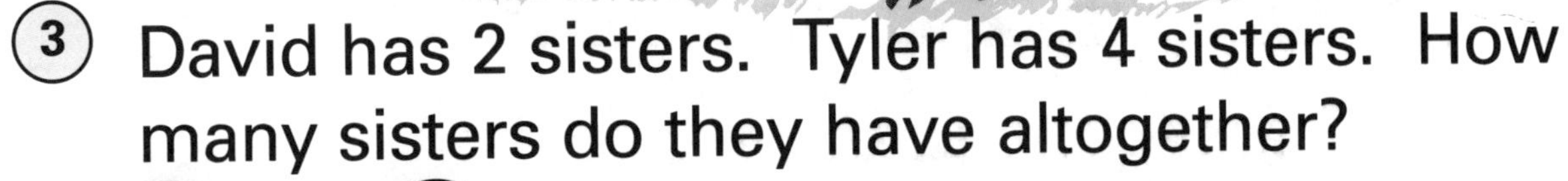

③ David has 2 sisters. Tyler has 4 sisters. How many sisters do they have altogether?

___ + ___ = ___ sisters

Wendy picked 4 oranges. Eva gave Wendy 3 more oranges. How many oranges did Wendy have altogether?

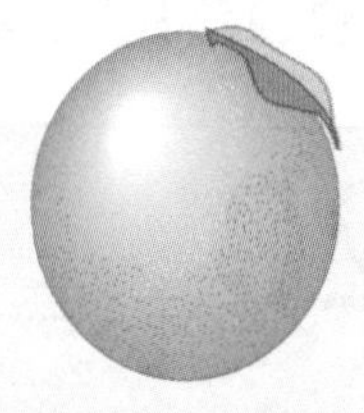

____ + ____ = ____ oranges

Amanda read 3 books. Megan read 5 books. How many books did they read altogether?

____ + ____ = ____ books

④ **Write the answers.**

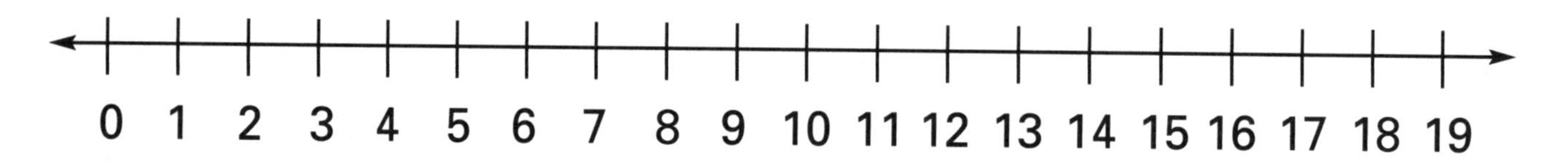

2	7	0	6	2	1
+5	+6	+3	+5	+8	+2

9	5	9	9	0	3
+7	+4	+0	+3	+7	+4

PLACE VALUE

① **Write the numbers in the blanks.**

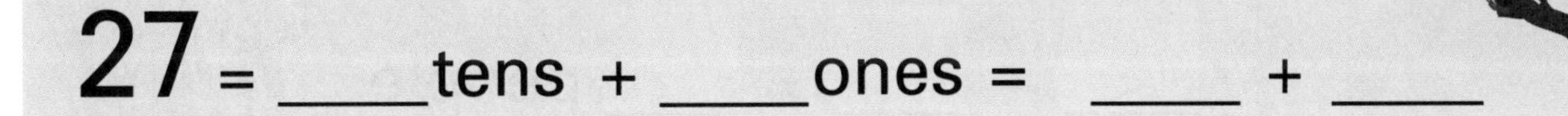

27 = ____ tens + ____ ones = ____ + ____

51 = ____ tens + ____ one = ____ + ____

43 = ____ tens + ____ ones = ____ + ____

68 = ____ tens + ____ ones = ____ + ____

② **Write the number for each.**

two ____

seven ____

three ____

five ____

nine ____

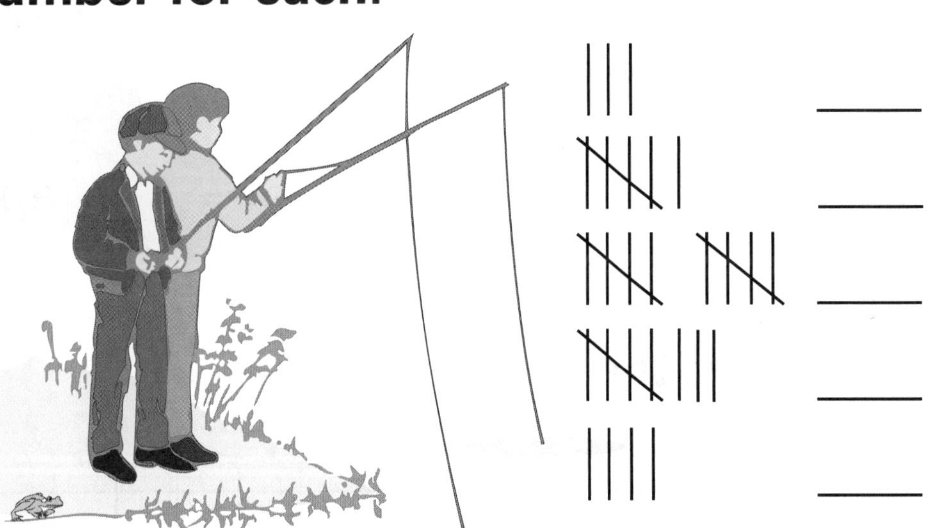

③ **Counting by 10's, write the number that comes after.**

30 ___ 50 ___ 10 ___ 80 ___

40 ___ 20 ___ 60 ___ 70 ___

④ Janice has 4 people in her family. Jerry has 4 people in his family. How many people are in the two families altogether?

☐ + ☐ = ☐ people

Nancy has 2 kittens. June has 1 kitten. How many kittens do they have altogether?

☐ + ☐ = ☐ kittens

The teacher has 2 apples. Bill gave her 2 more apples. How many apples does the teacher have altogether?

☐ + ☐ = ☐ apples

⑤ **Write the answers.**

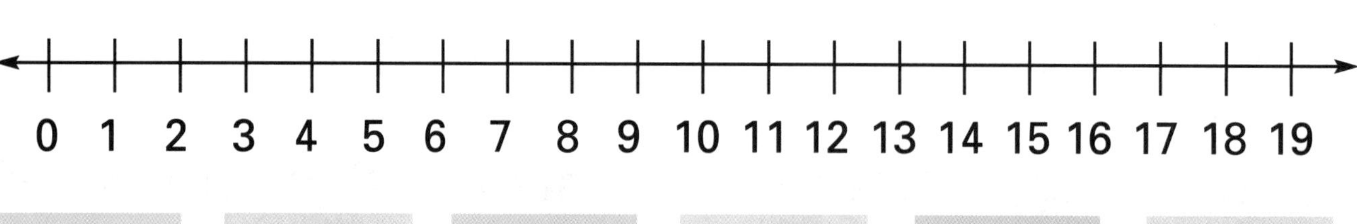

$$\begin{array}{r} 3 \\ +9 \\ \hline \end{array} \quad \begin{array}{r} 9 \\ +8 \\ \hline \end{array} \quad \begin{array}{r} 6 \\ +9 \\ \hline \end{array} \quad \begin{array}{r} 7 \\ +5 \\ \hline \end{array} \quad \begin{array}{r} 4 \\ +6 \\ \hline \end{array} \quad \begin{array}{r} 8 \\ +5 \\ \hline \end{array}$$

MONEY – PENNY

Penny

1 cent

1¢

① **Count the pennies. Write the number in the box.**

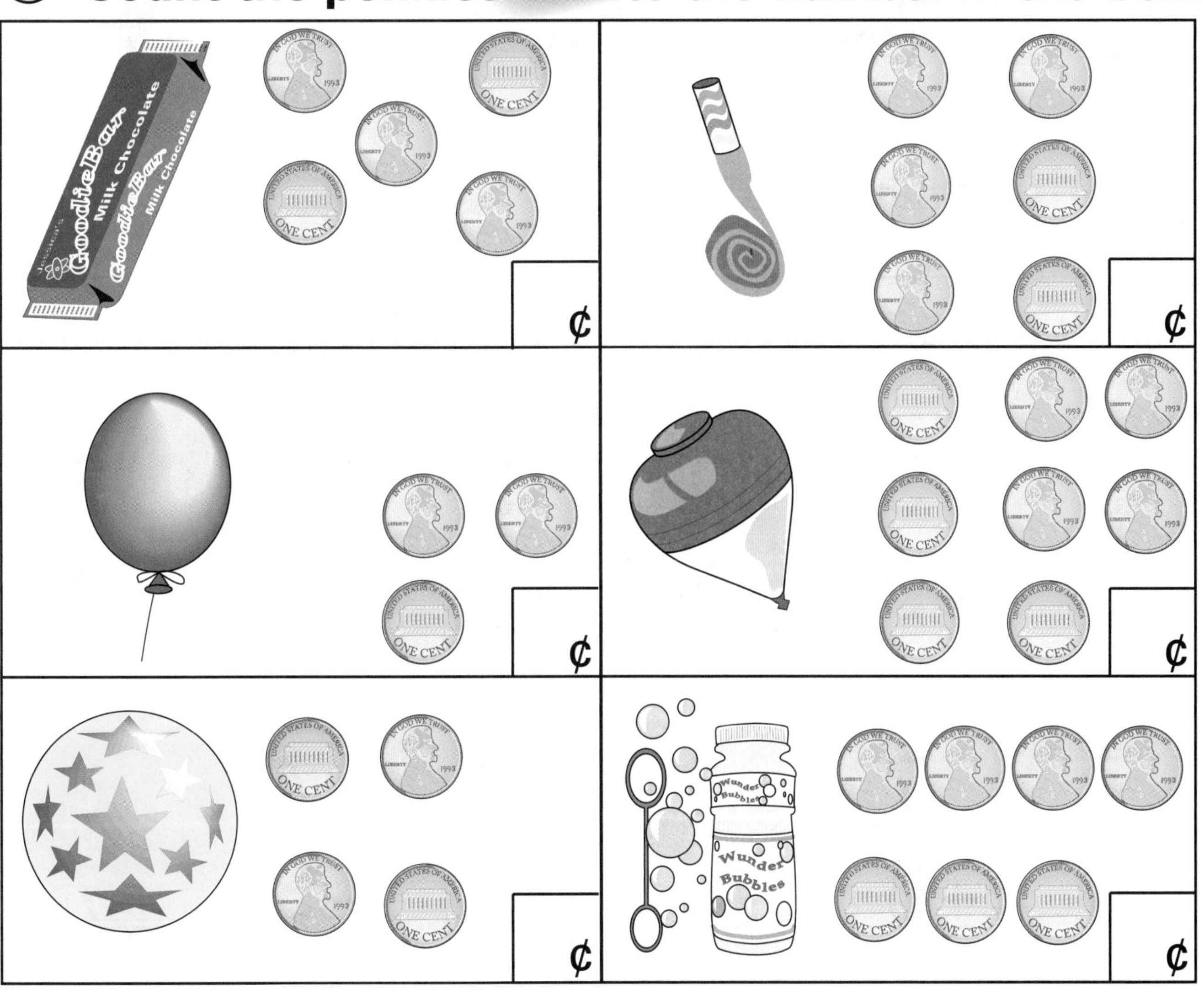

② Write the numbers in the blanks.

12 = ____ ten + ____ ones = ____ + ____

76 = ____ tens + ____ ones = ____ + ____

35 = ____ tens + ____ ones = ____ + ____

89 = ____ tens + ____ ones = ____ + ____

42 = ____ tens + ____ ones = ____ + ____

③ Write the answers.

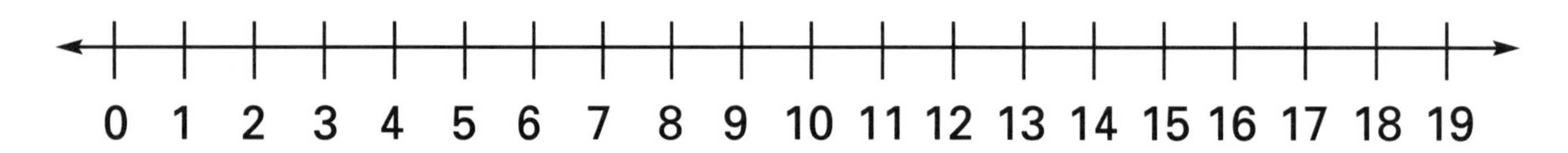

$$\begin{array}{r}3\\+2\\\hline\end{array}\quad\begin{array}{r}3\\+8\\\hline\end{array}\quad\begin{array}{r}1\\+5\\\hline\end{array}\quad\begin{array}{r}5\\+8\\\hline\end{array}\quad\begin{array}{r}8\\+0\\\hline\end{array}\quad\begin{array}{r}2\\+4\\\hline\end{array}$$

$$\begin{array}{r}7\\+8\\\hline\end{array}\quad\begin{array}{r}7\\+0\\\hline\end{array}\quad\begin{array}{r}1\\+3\\\hline\end{array}\quad\begin{array}{r}2\\+6\\\hline\end{array}\quad\begin{array}{r}4\\+3\\\hline\end{array}\quad\begin{array}{r}6\\+7\\\hline\end{array}$$

TIME – HALF HOUR

A half hour is 30 minutes.

The long hand is on the 12 at 3:00.

The long hand is on the 6 at 3:30.

① Write the time.

:

:

:

:

:

:

:

:

:

:

:

:

② Write the answers.

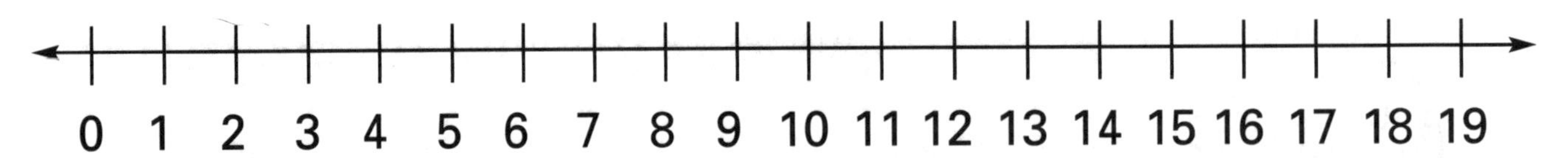

2 cents +2 cents ___ cents	6 ¢ +2 ¢ ___ ¢	5 ¢ +1 ¢ ___ ¢	1 cents +8 cents ___ cents
9 cents +6 cents ___ cents	7 ¢ +1 ¢ ___ ¢	9 ¢ +4 ¢ ___ ¢	6 pennies +3 pennies ___ pennies

③ Write the numbers in the blanks.

7 = ____ tens + ____ ones = ____ + ____

31 = ____ tens + ____ one = ____ + ____

84 = ____ tens + ____ ones = ____ + ____

50 = ____ tens + ____ ones = ____ + ____

MONEY – DIME

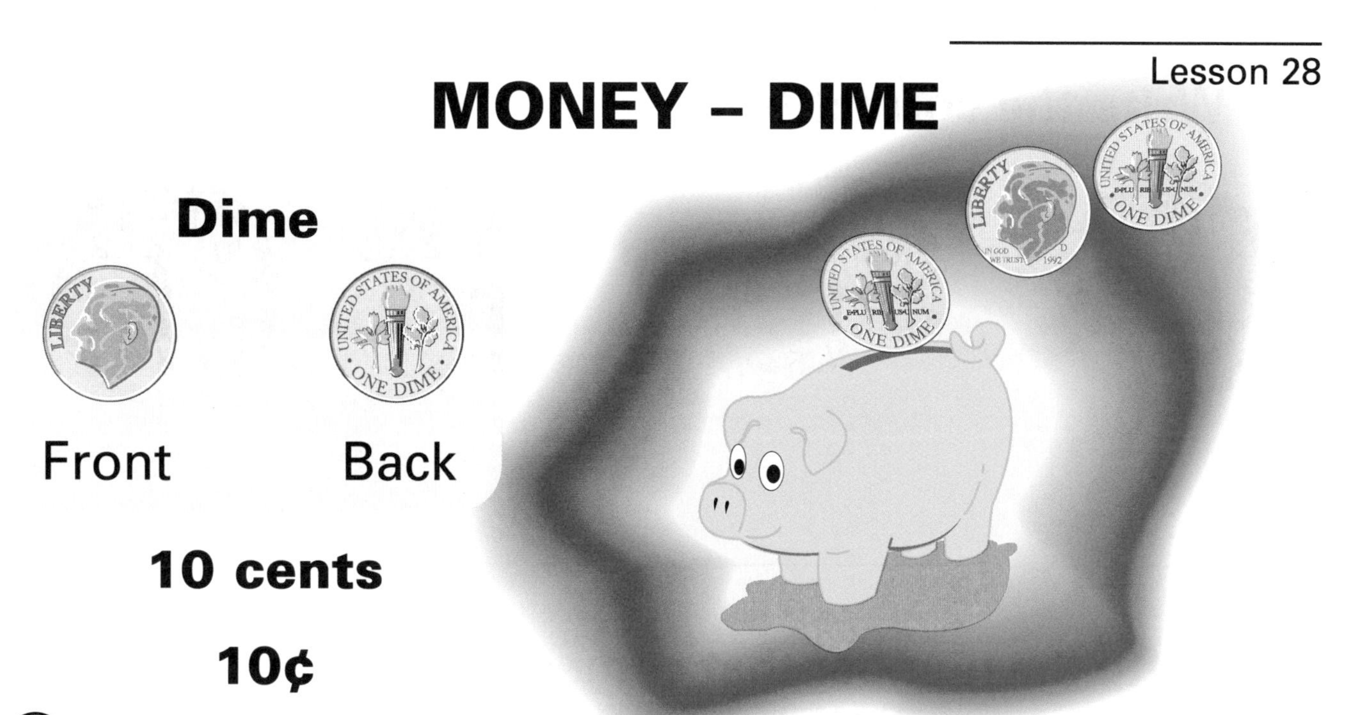

Dime

Front Back

10 cents

10¢

① **Count the dimes by 10's. Write the number.**

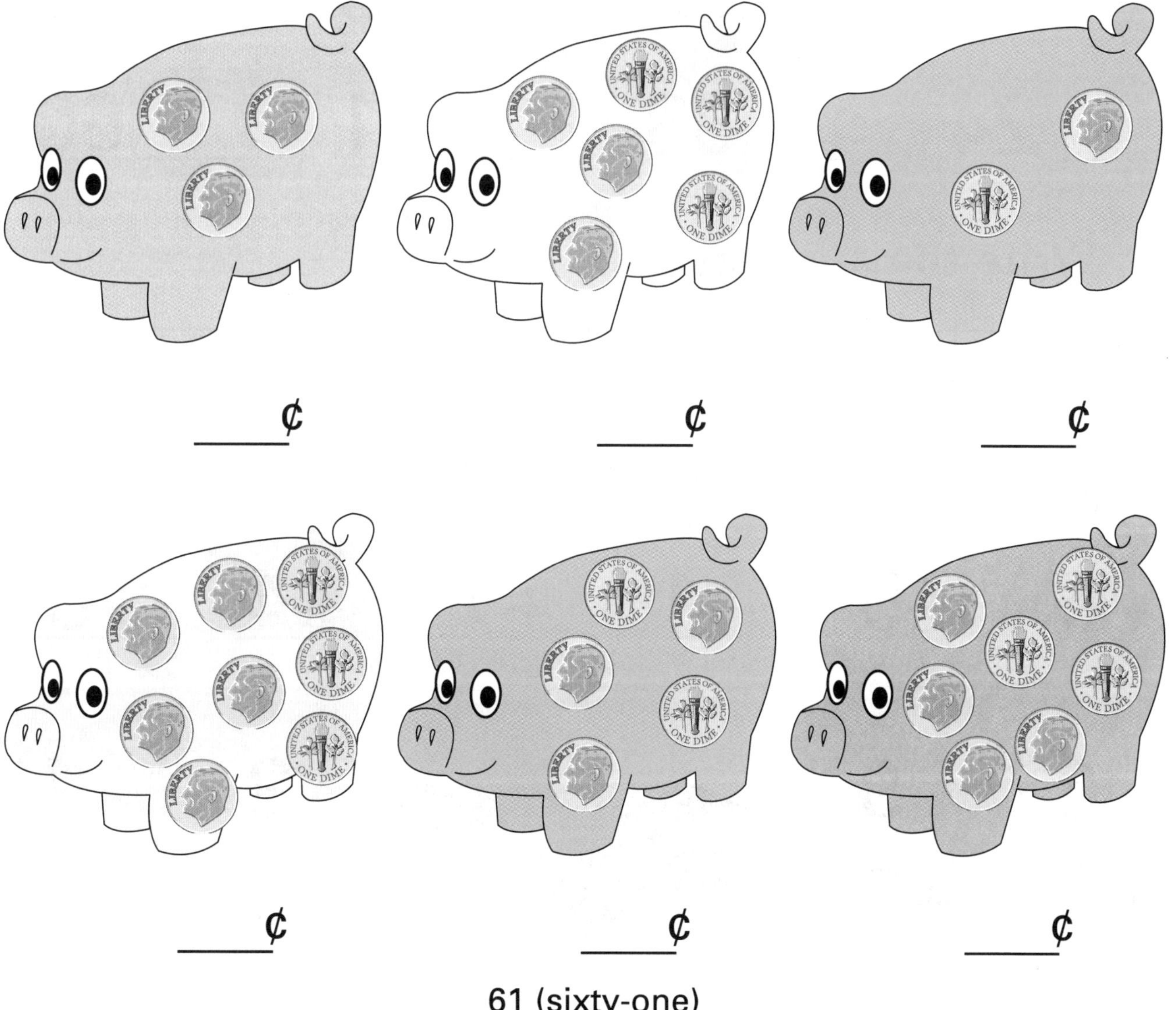

_____¢ _____¢ _____¢

_____¢ _____¢ _____¢

② Write the correct time.

___:___ ___:___ ___:___ ___:___

③ Write the number that comes before.

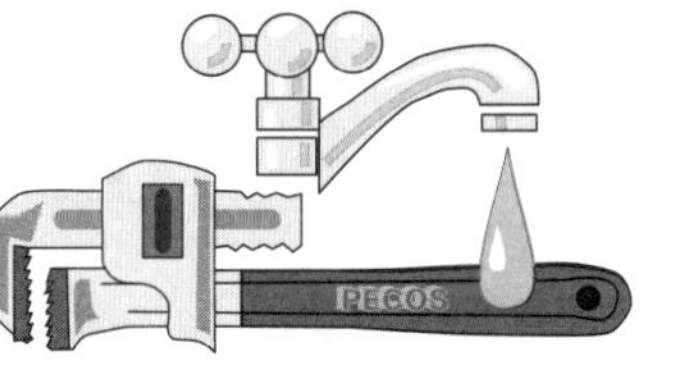

___ 35	___ 52	___ 18	___ 76
___ 24	___ 83	___ 41	___ 60

④ Write the answers.

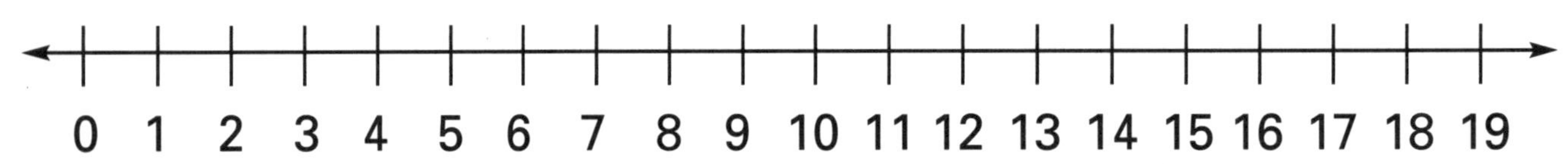

$4 + 6 =$ ___	$5 + 5 =$ ___	$2 + 1 =$ ___	$6 + 7 =$ ___	$7 + 4 =$ ___	$8 + 8 =$ ___

$6 + 0 =$ ___	$9 + 2 =$ ___	$3 + 3 =$ ___	$1 + 7 =$ ___

MONEY – PENNIES AND DIMES

① **Count the dimes by 10's. Count the pennies. Write the value of each set.**

10 pennies = 1 dime

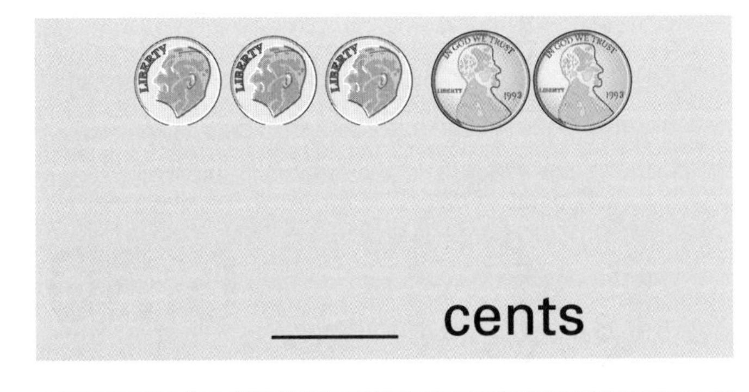

_____ cents

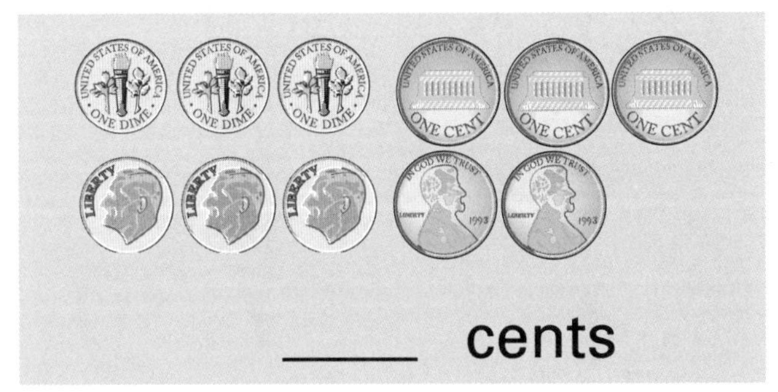

_____ cents

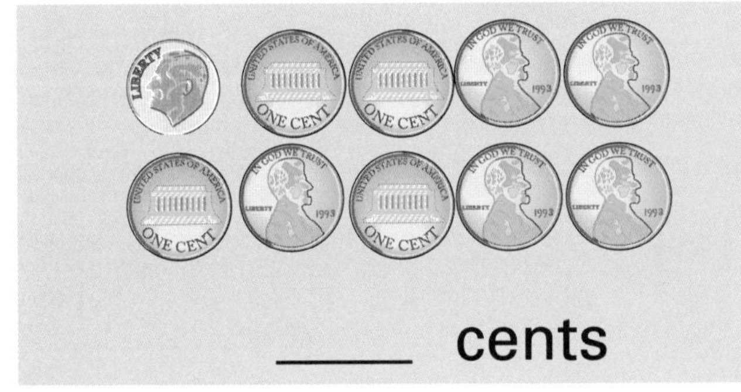

_____ cents

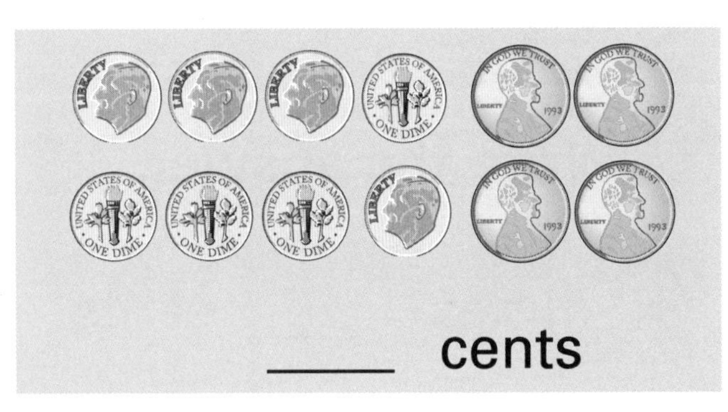

_____ cents

② **Write = or ≠ between each set.**

1+4 ___ 6	3+5 ___ 8	7+4 ___ 11
6+2 ___ 8	8+3 ___ 11	9+5 ___ 13
3+4 ___ 7	6+4 ___ 9	8+6 ___ 15

③ Draw a line to match the time with the clock.

9:30

2:30

7:30

4:30

12:30

6:30

④ Write the answer.

4 dimes = ____ cents	8 dimes = ____ cents
3 dimes = ____ cents	1 dime = ____ cents
7 dimes = ____ cents	5 dimes = ____ cents
9 dimes = ____ cents	2 dimes = ____ cents
6 dimes = ____ cents	10 dimes = ____ cents

TEST 3

① Write the correct time. **4 pts. total for this exercise.**

___:___ ___:___ ___:___ ___:___

② Counting by 5's, write the number that comes after.

8 pts. total for this exercise.

40 ___ 25 ___ 75 ___ 60 ___

10 ___ 90 ___ 35 ___ 55 ___

③ Lisa baked 5 cakes. Rose gave Lisa 1 cake she baked. How many cakes did Lisa have altogether?

2 pts. total for this exercise.

___ + ___ = ___ cakes

Bob sang 2 songs. Dan sang 2 songs. How many songs did they sing altogether?

___ + ___ = ___ songs

④ Draw a line to match each set. 10 pts.

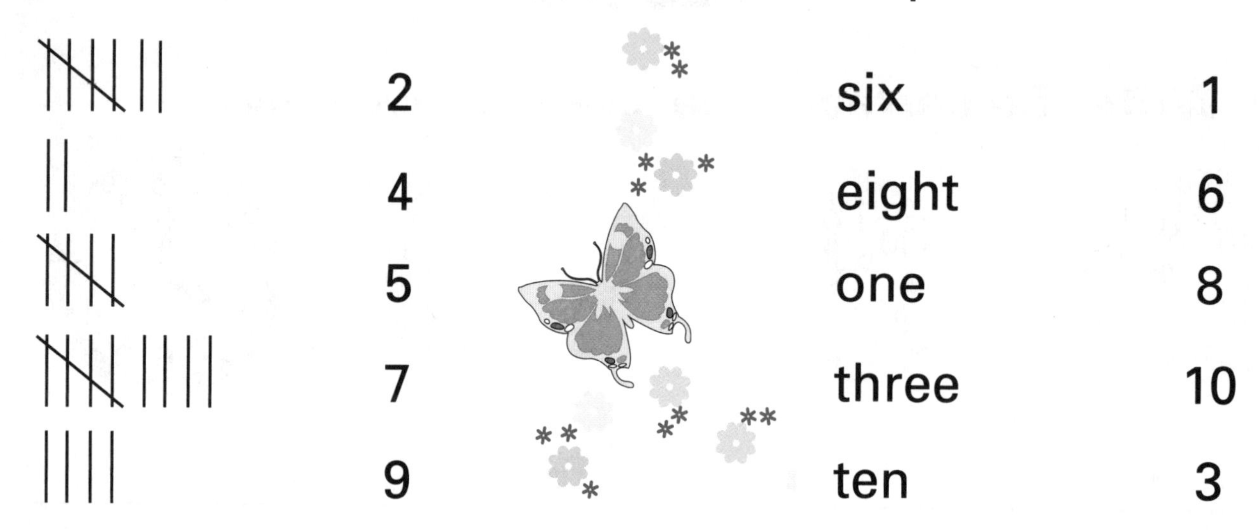

2		six	1
4		eight	6
5		one	8
7		three	10
9		ten	3

⑤ Write the answers. 16 pts. total for this exercise.

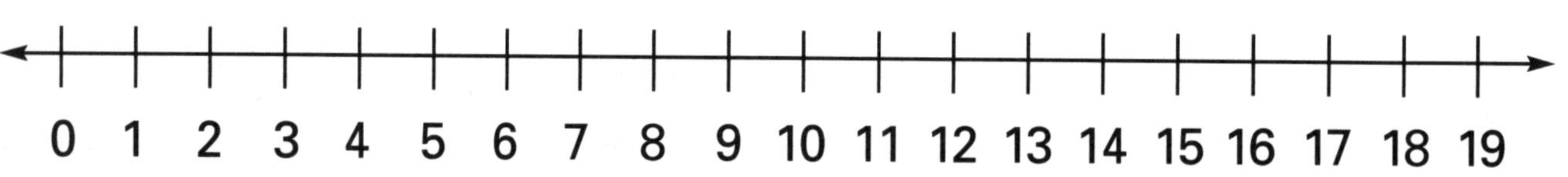

1 +3	7 +0	2 +4	3 +5	4 +1	9 +9
6 +2	4 +7	5 +9	6 +8	9 +4	0 +1
8 +6	7 +2			4 +4	4 +2

40 pts. Total

CALENDAR – DAYS OF THE WEEK

① **Circle the correct answer.**

October

Sunday	Monday	Tuesday	Wednesday	Thursday	Friday	Saturday
			1	2	3	4
5	6	7	8	9	10	11
12	13	14	15	16	17	18
19	20	21	22	23	24	25
26	27	28	29	30	31	

What is the month on the calendar?
October May August

What day of the week is October 1?
Monday Tuesday Wednesday

What day of the week is October 10?
Thursday Friday Saturday

What day of the week is October 27?
Monday Tuesday Wednesday

What day of the week is October 25?
Thursday Friday Saturday

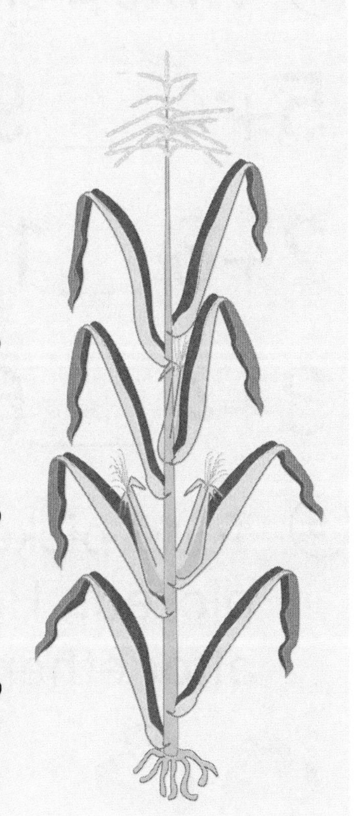

② Draw the short hand for each clock.

2:30

8:30

4:30

10:30

③ Write the number that comes before.

___ 16	___ 48	___ 25	___ 99
___ 32	___ 80	___ 3	___ 74

④ Write = or ≠ between each set.

5+4 ___ 9	7+1 ___ 9	8+4 ___ 11
2+8 ___ 10	6+3 ___ 9	9+5 ___ 14
3+4 ___ 6	5+7 ___ 13	6+2 ___ 8

⑤ Todd picked 7 apples. Dick gave Todd 1 apple he picked. How many apples did Todd have altogether?

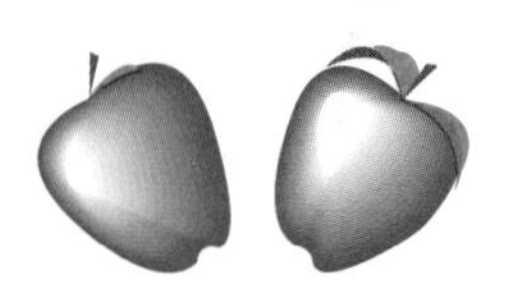

___ + ___ = ___ apples

INCHES

① **Write the number of inches for each object.**

This leaf is 2 inches long.

2 inches

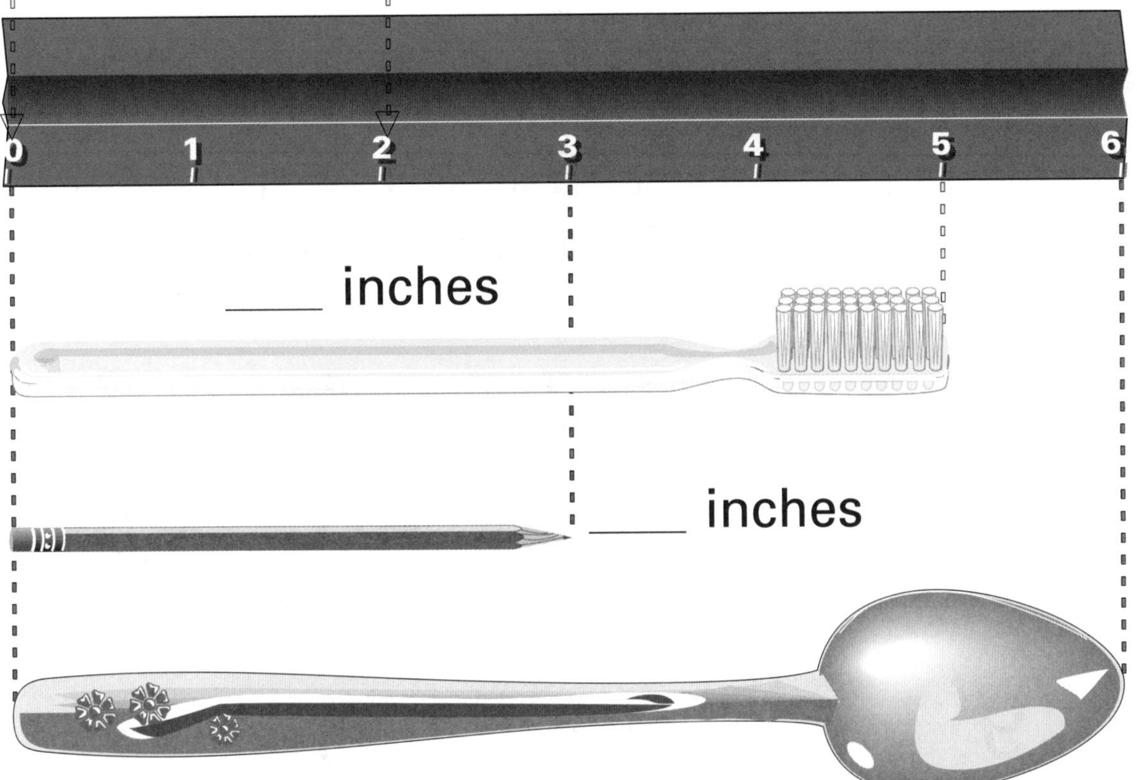

____ inches

____ inches

____ inches

② **Write the number that comes before.**

____ 34	____ 75	____ 12	____ 68
____ 57	____ 20	____ 49	____ 81
____ 8	____ 93	____ 28	____ 44

③ **Write = or ≠ between each set.**

1+5 ___ 7	2+6 ___ 8	3+5 ___ 7
4+7 ___ 11	5+7 ___ 13	6+6 ___ 12
7+3 ___ 10	8+7 ___ 16	9+4 ___ 14

④ **Write the answers.**

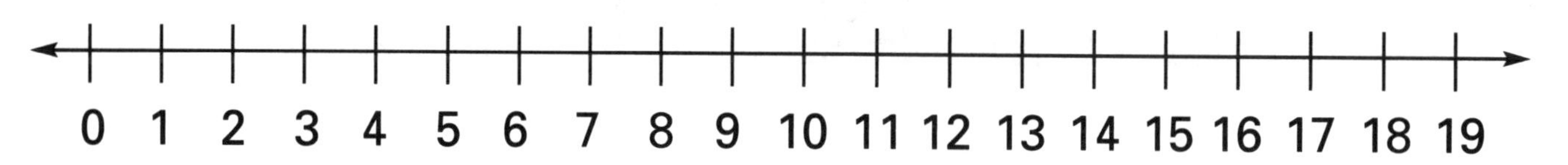

$$\begin{array}{r} 8 \\ +2 \\ \hline \end{array} \quad \begin{array}{r} 5 \\ +7 \\ \hline \end{array} \quad \begin{array}{r} 2 \\ +8 \\ \hline \end{array} \quad \begin{array}{r} 7 \\ +9 \\ \hline \end{array} \quad \begin{array}{r} 4 \\ +8 \\ \hline \end{array} \quad \begin{array}{r} 6 \\ +9 \\ \hline \end{array}$$

$$\begin{array}{r} 6 \\ +5 \\ \hline \end{array} \quad \begin{array}{r} 9 \\ +0 \\ \hline \end{array} \quad \begin{array}{r} 7 \\ +8 \\ \hline \end{array} \quad \begin{array}{r} 5 \\ +2 \\ \hline \end{array} \quad \begin{array}{r} 8 \\ +1 \\ \hline \end{array} \quad \begin{array}{r} 7 \\ +7 \\ \hline \end{array}$$

$$\begin{array}{r} 8 \\ +7 \\ \hline \end{array} \quad \begin{array}{r} 7 \\ +1 \\ \hline \end{array}$$

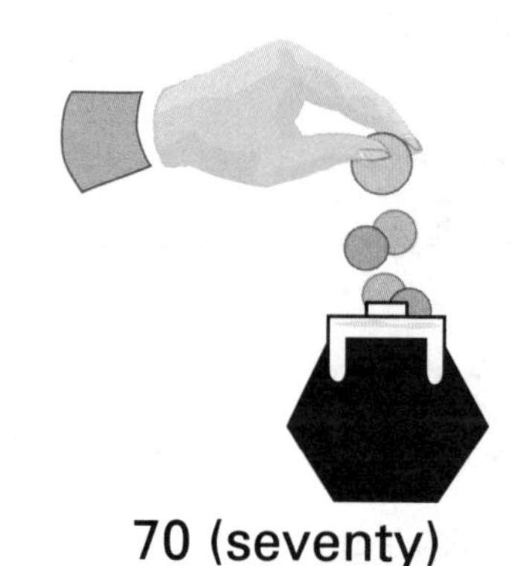

$$\begin{array}{r} 4 \\ +5 \\ \hline \end{array} \quad \begin{array}{r} 7 \\ +6 \\ \hline \end{array}$$

NUMBER ORDER – BEFORE BY 2'S

① **When counting by 2's, write the number that comes before.**

___ 24	___ 86	___ 76	___ 10
___ 72	___ 58	___ 34	___ 92

② **Count the dimes by 10's. Count the pennies. Write the value of each set.**

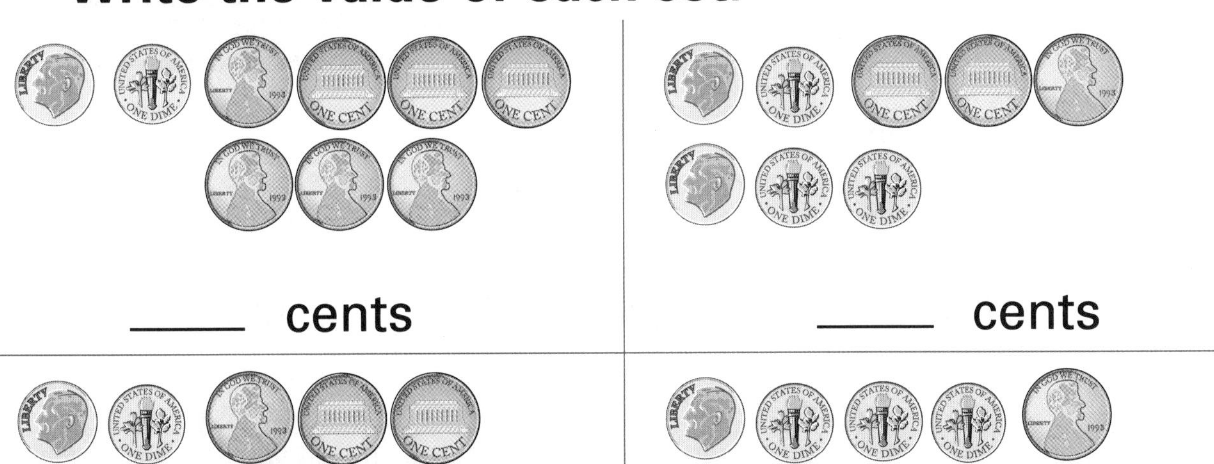

____ cents ____ cents

____ cents ____ cents

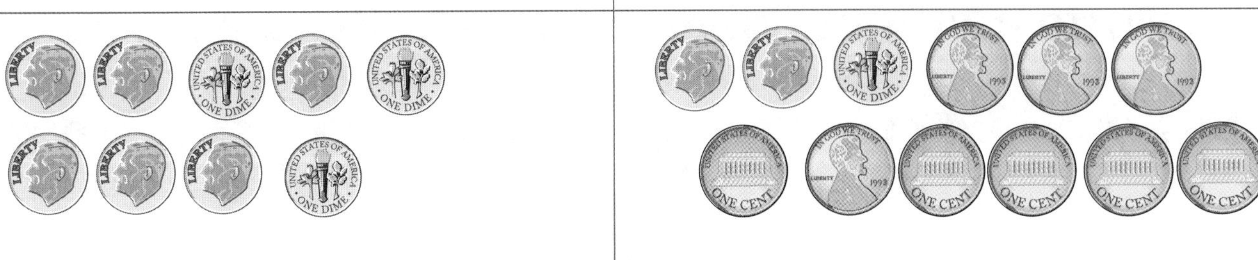

____ cents ____ cents

③ Measure the objects.

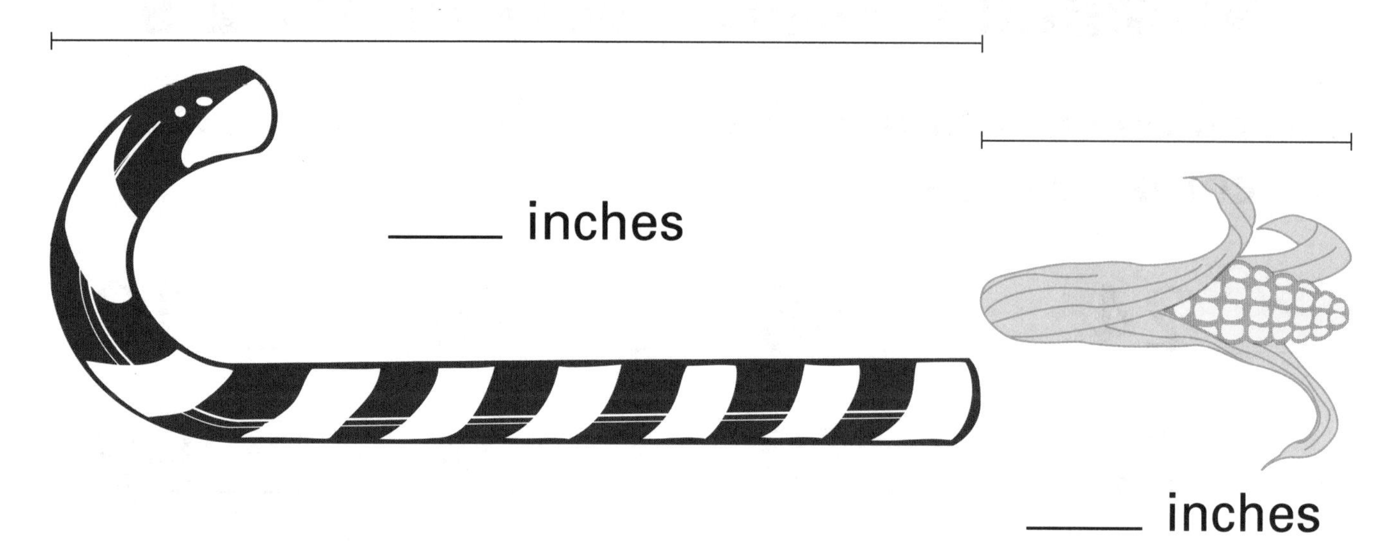

____ inches

____ inches

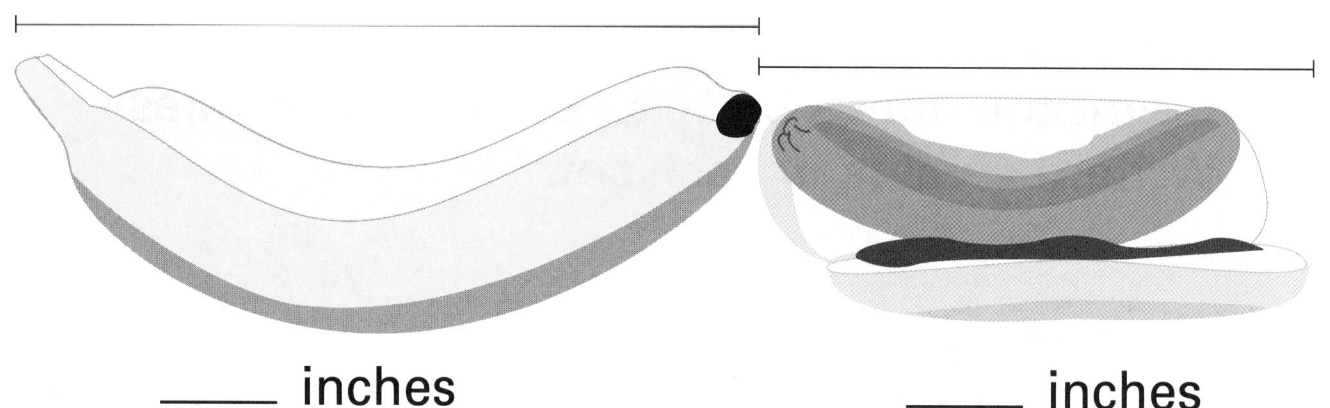

____ inches

____ inches

④ When counting by 4's, write the missing numbers.

4 ____ 12 ____ ____ 24 ____

32 36 ____ 44 ____ ____ 56

⑤ Write < or > between each set. Read each set.

5+4 ____ 10   7+6 ____ 14   3+9 ____ 11

8+2 ____ 11   2+5 ____ 6   4+7 ____ 12

MONEY – NICKELS

Nickel

Front

Back

5 cents
5¢

1 **Count the nickels by 5's. Draw a line to match the nickels to cents.**

35¢

20¢

40¢

10¢

25¢

30¢

15¢

2 Measure the objects.

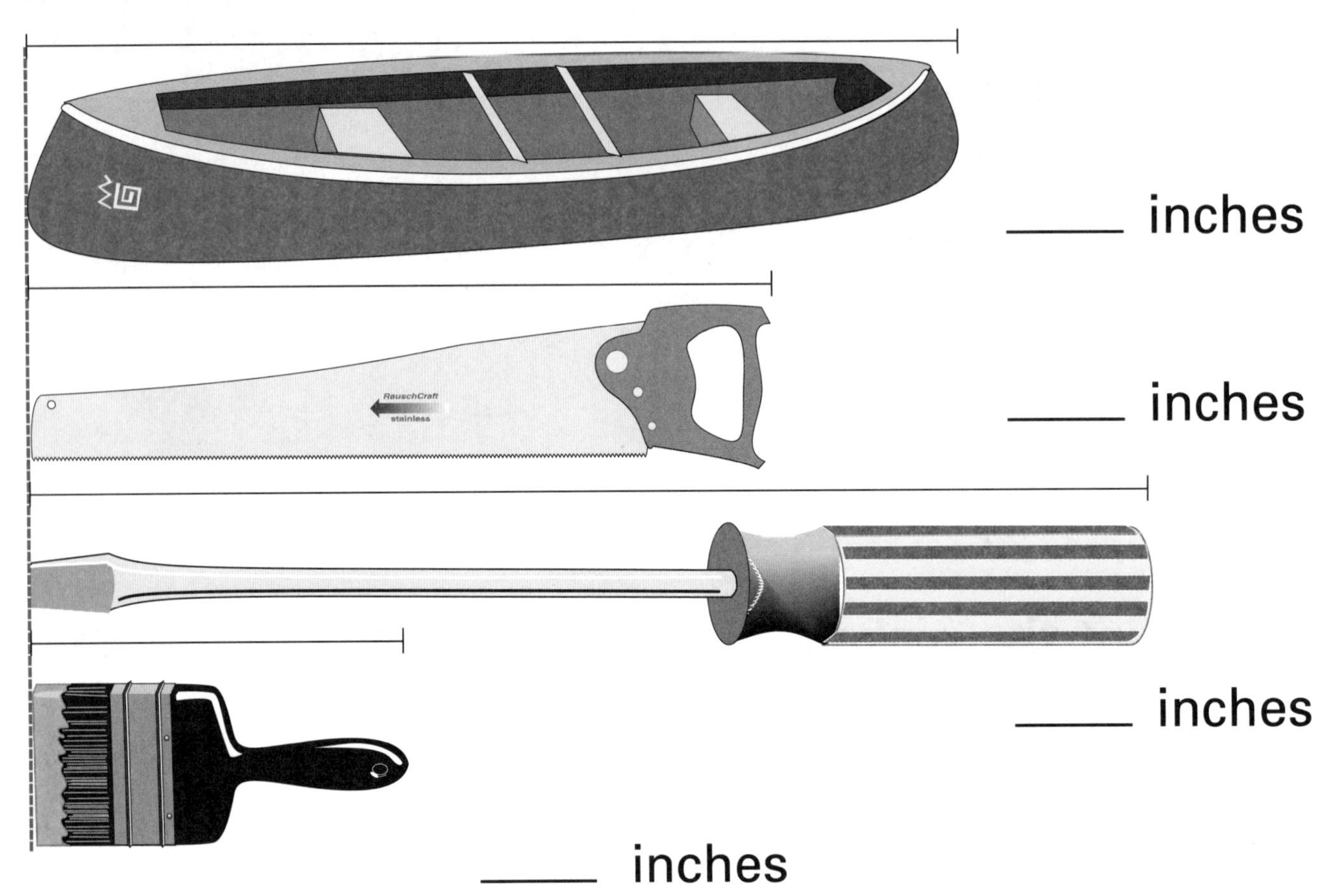

3 Counting by 2's, write the number that comes before.

____ 36	____ 58	____ 24	____ 92
____ 40	____ 14	____ 66	____ 88

4 Write < or > between each set.

four ____ 5	one ____ 0	two ____ 6
five ____ 4	ten ____ 11	three ____ 5
six ____ 3	eight ____ 7	seven ____ 9

NAMING FRACTIONS

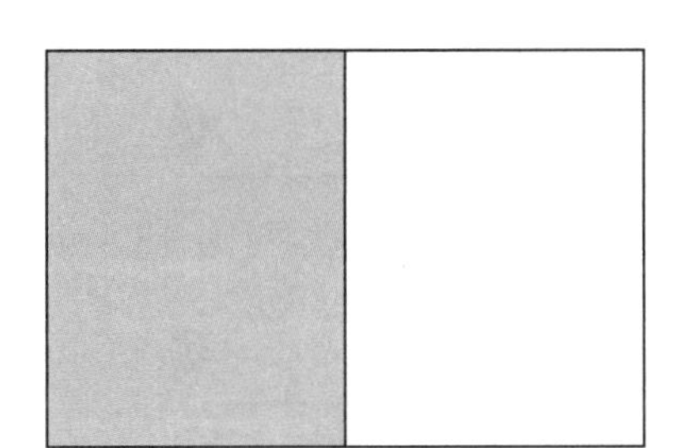
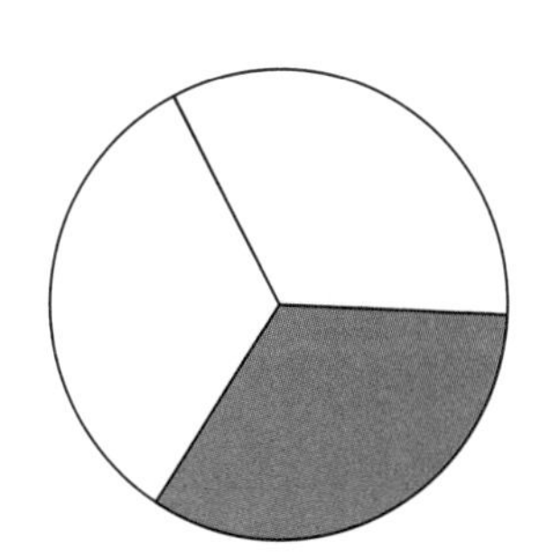
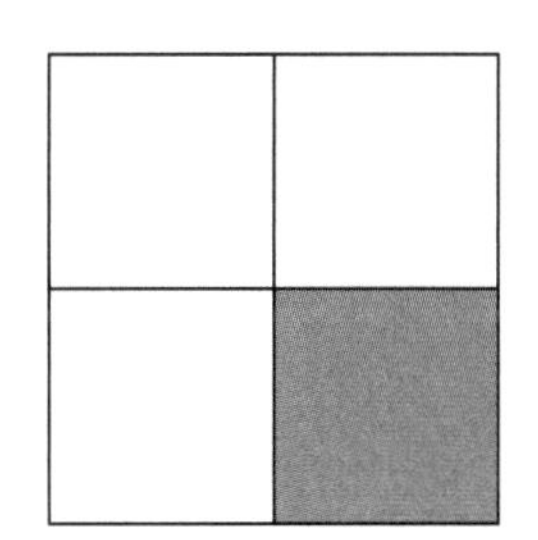
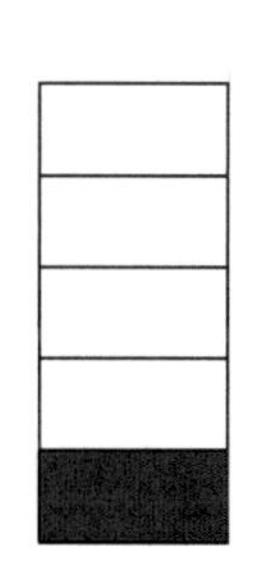

$\frac{1}{2}$ $\frac{1}{3}$ $\frac{1}{4}$ $\frac{1}{5}$

① Write the fractional part that is shaded.

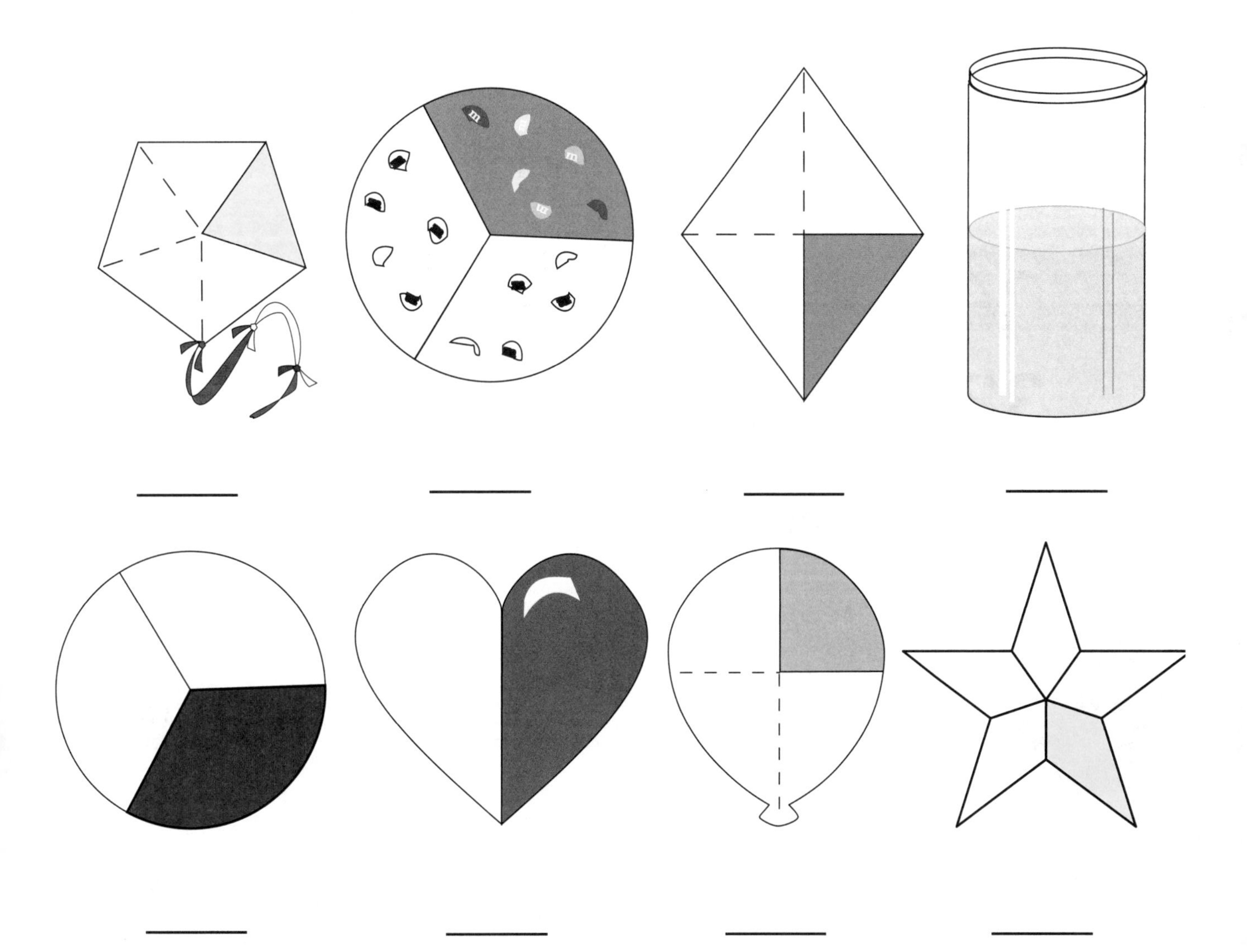

② **Count the nickels by 5's. Write the answer in cents.**

____¢

____¢

____¢

____¢

____¢

③ **Counting by 2's, write the number that comes before.**

____ 52	____ 26	____ 74	____ 60
____ 38	____ 84	____ 46	____ 10

④ **Measure the objects.**

LOLLYPOP BRAND

____ inches

____ inches

WORD NUMBERS 11-20

① **Draw a line to match the number and the word number.**

twelve	11
fourteen	12
fifteen	13
eleven	14
thirteen	15

eighteen	16
sixteen	17
seventeen	18
twenty	19
nineteen	20

② **Count the nickels by 5's. Write the answer.**

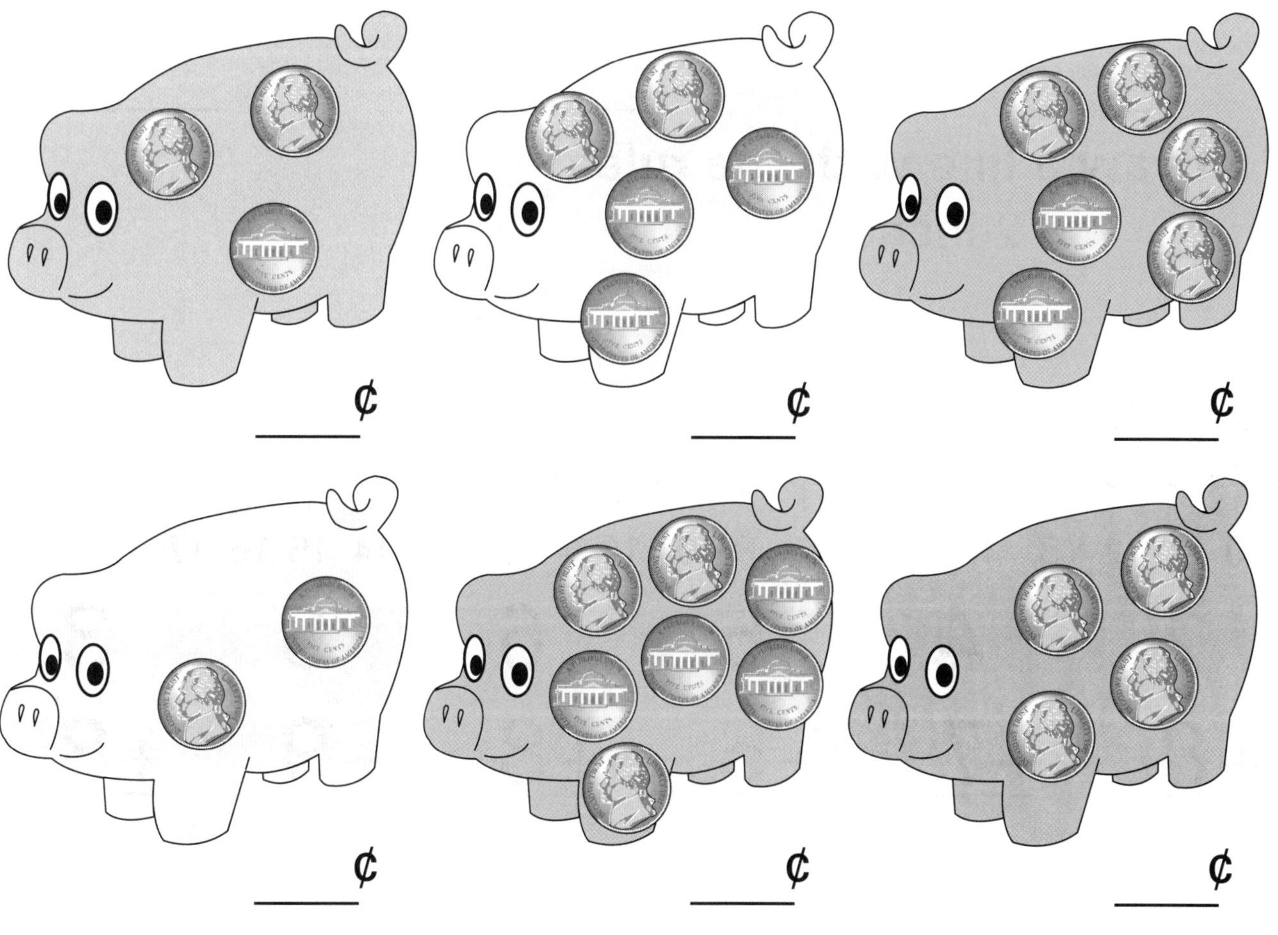

③ Write the fractional part that is shaded.

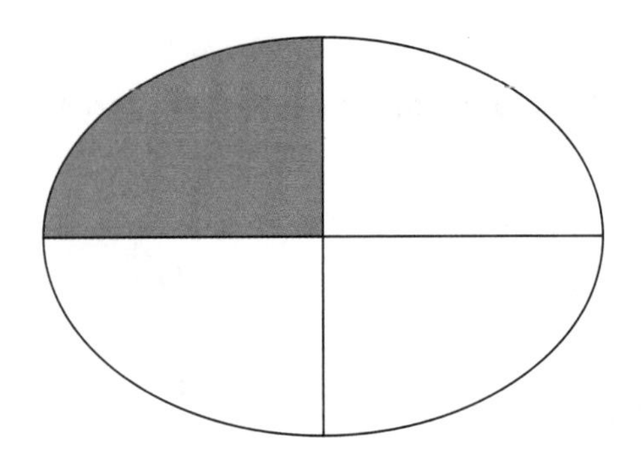

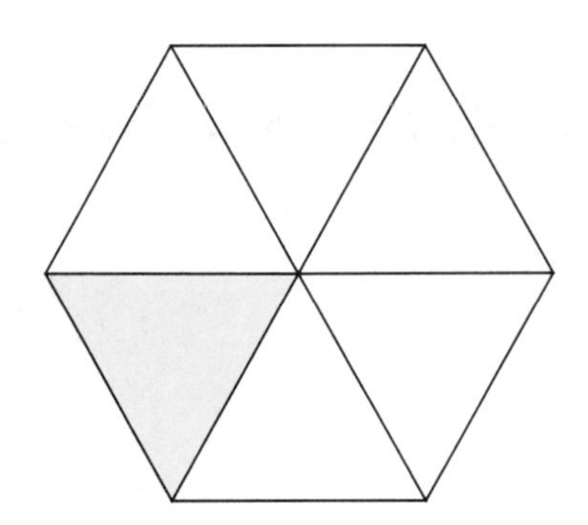

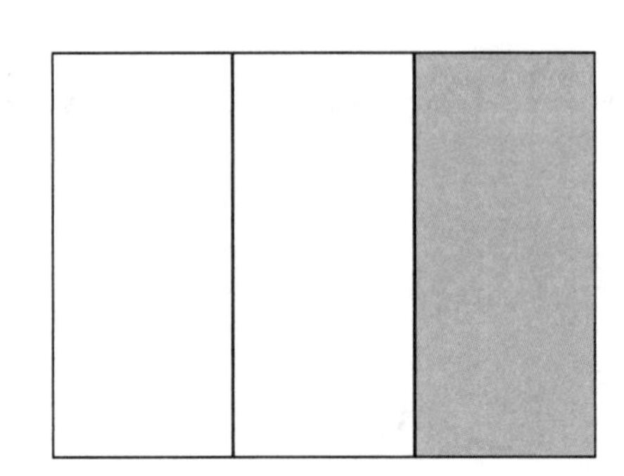

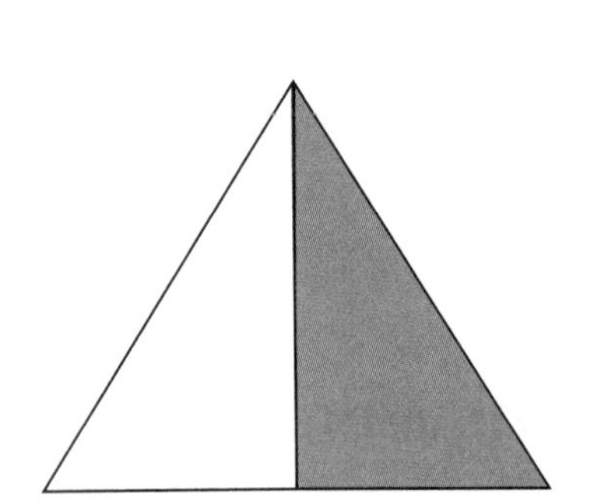

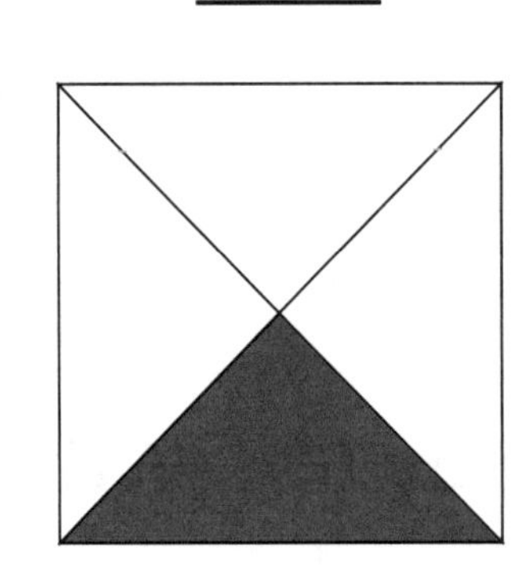

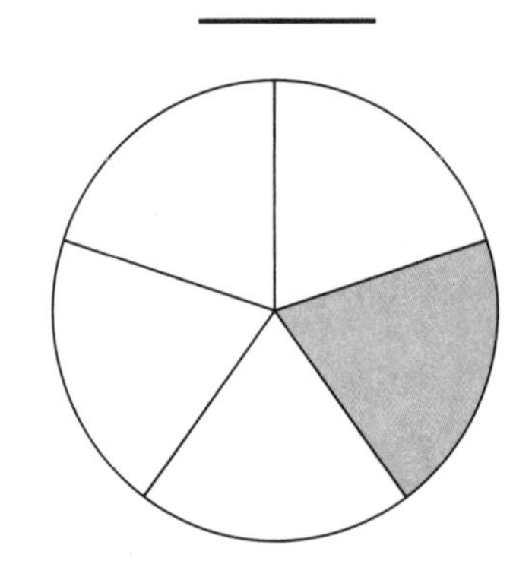

④ Draw a line with the ruler.

2 inches .

4 inches .

⑤ Write the answers.

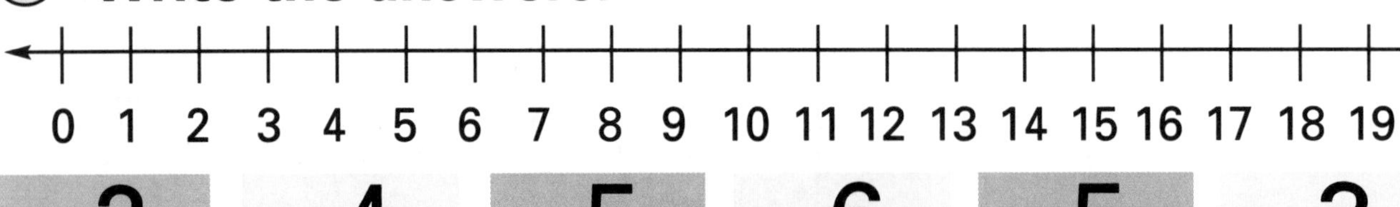

2	4	5	6	5	3
+8	+7	+5	+8	+9	+8

ADDITION – DOUBLE DIGIT

tens' place ones' place	tens' place ones' place	tens' place ones' place
36	52	43
+ 12	+ 34	+ 54
48	86	97

① **Write the answers.**

22 +31	46 +41	72 +16	34 +51	61 +18	82 +17
72 +20	45 +30	53 +24	32 +24	77 +11	60 +35
23 +54	45 +23	60 +24	52 +44	14 +31	16 +50

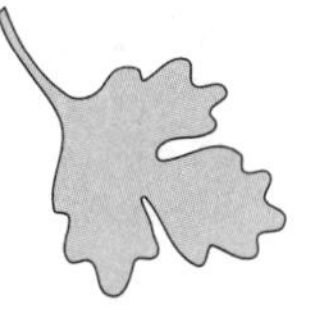

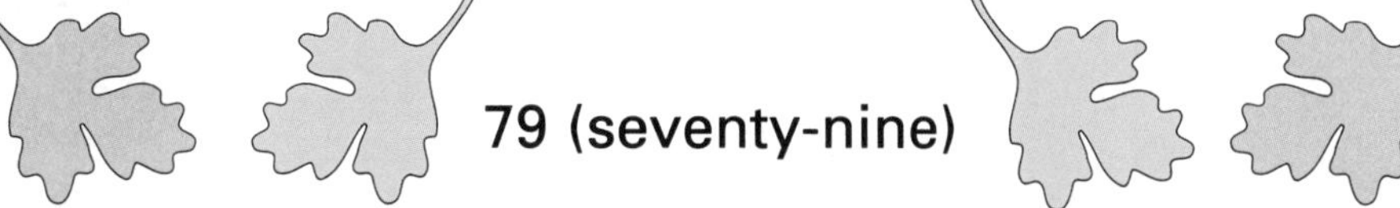
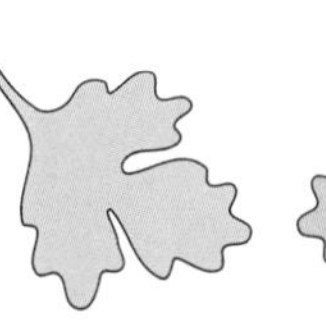
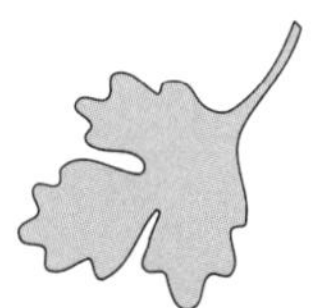

② **Counting by 2's, write the number that comes before.**

___ 14 ___ 56 ___ 38 ___ 20

___ 96 ___ 44 ___ 82 ___ 60

③ **Count the nickels by 5's. Count the pennies. Write the cents.**

___ ¢

___ ¢

___ ¢

___ ¢

④ Chris picked 8 flowers. Kim picked 3 more and gave them to Chris. How many did Chris have altogether?

___ ___ ___ flowers

ADDITION – HORIZONTAL AND VERTICAL

tens' place	ones' place
2	4
+ 1	3
3	7

① **Write the problems vertically. Write the answers.**

17 + 42 =

+

22 + 51 =

+

12 + 53 =

+

83 + 14 =

+

66 + 22 =

+

14 + 72 =

+

② **Count the tens by 10's. Count the ones. Write the number.**

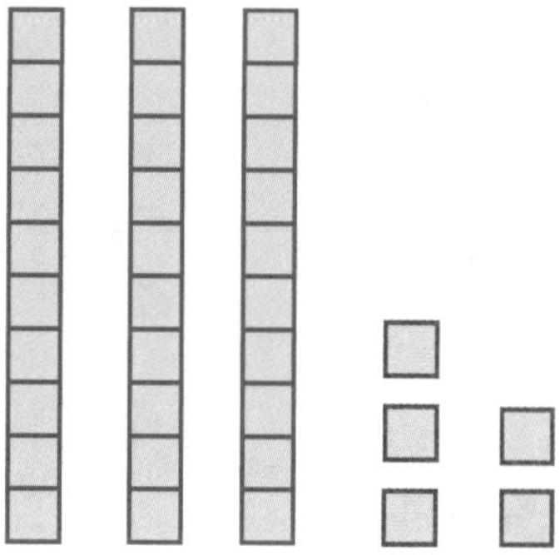

____ ____ ____

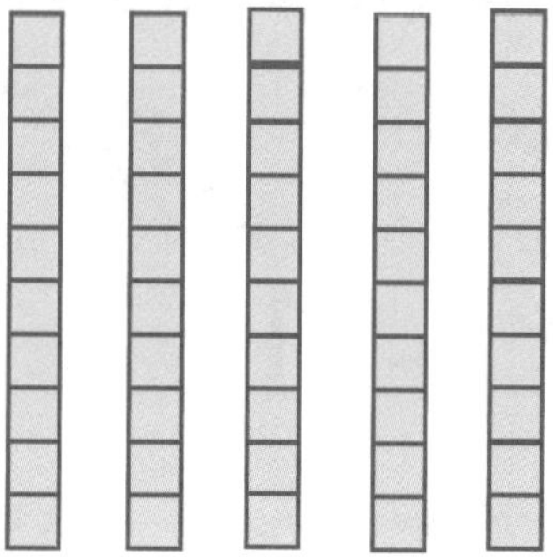

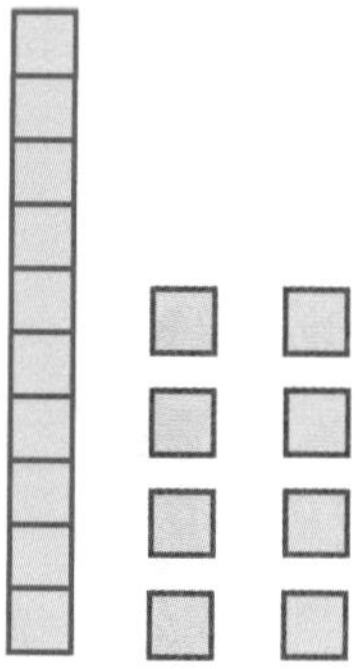

③ **Count the nickels by 5's. Count the pennies by 1's. Circle the correct answer.**

19¢ 34¢ 23¢

19¢ 43¢ 23¢

35¢ 7¢ 70¢

18¢ 41¢ 13¢

30¢ 55¢ 10¢

④ **Counting by 2's, write the number that comes before.**

___ 84 ___ 36 ___ 52 ___ 18

___ 40 ___ 94 ___ 28 ___ 62

FRACTIONS – ONE HALF

1 Draw a line to divide each object in half.

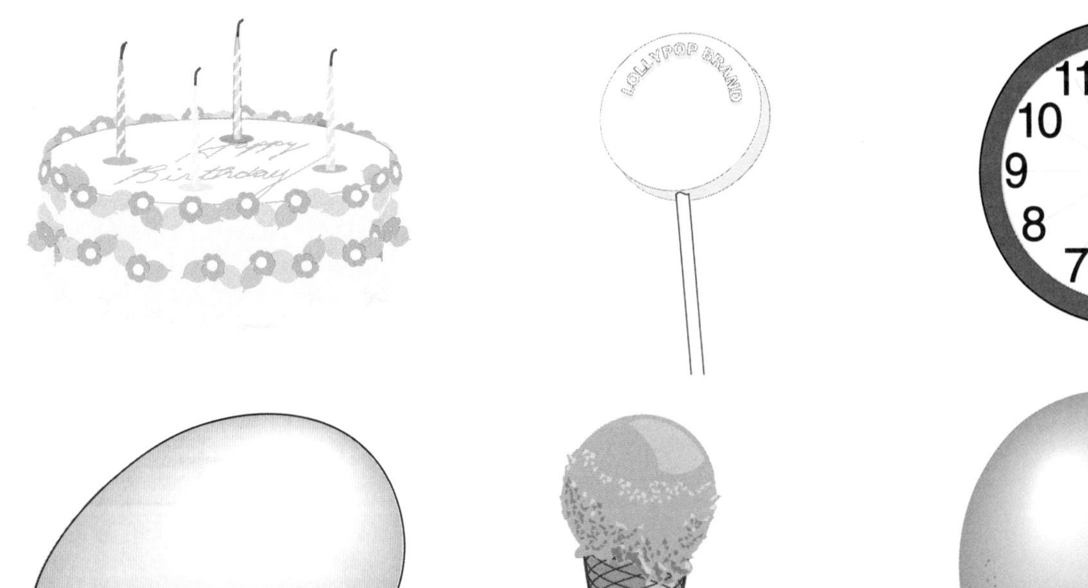

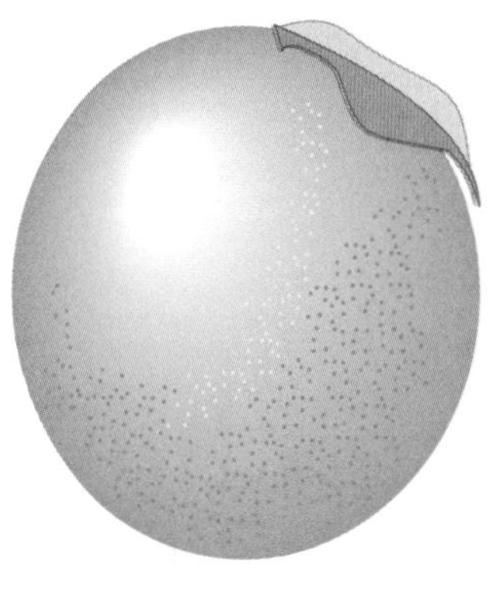

2 Write the numbers in the blanks.

90 + 1 = ___	80 + 0 = ___
50 + 4 = ___	40 + 6 = ___
30 + 8 = ___	60 + 7 = ___
70 + 5 = ___	10 + 3 = ___
20 + 9 = ___	30 + 2 = ___

③ **Write the problems vertically. Write the answers.**

$43 + 31 =$

+

$55 + 33 =$

+

$12 + 15 =$

+

$65 + 14 =$

+

$86 + 12 =$

+

$34 + 22 =$

+

$17 + 21 =$

+

$70 + 16 =$

+

④ Pat walked 2 blocks to the store. She then walked 7 blocks to her grandparents house. How many blocks did Pat walk altogether?

____ + ____ = ____ blocks

NUMBER ORDER – BEFORE AND AFTER

① **Write the number that comes before and after.**

___ 8 ___	___ 16 ___	___ 24 ___
___ 35 ___	___ 47 ___	___ 51 ___
___ 69 ___	___ 72 ___	___ 83 ___

② **Color one half ($\frac{1}{2}$) of each object.**

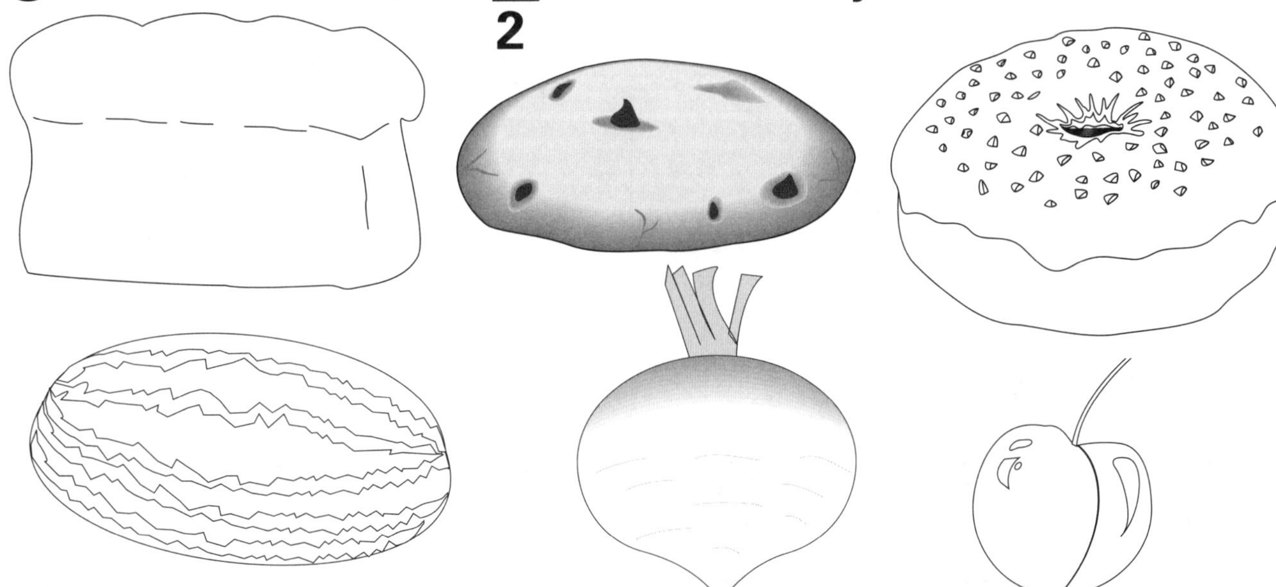

③ **Circle a set of 6 blocks. Circle a set of 10 beads.**

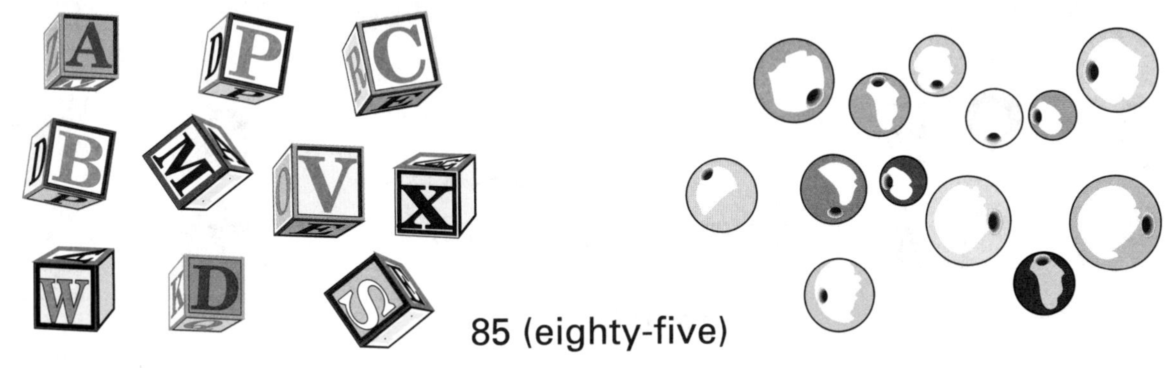

④ **Write the problems vertically. Write the answers.**

$83 + 15 =$

$$\begin{array}{r} \\ + \\ \hline \end{array}$$

$75 + 10 =$

$$\begin{array}{r} \\ + \\ \hline \end{array}$$

$52 + 25 =$

$$\begin{array}{r} \\ + \\ \hline \end{array}$$

$36 + 21 =$

$$\begin{array}{r} \\ + \\ \hline \end{array}$$

$77 + 12 =$

$$\begin{array}{r} \\ + \\ \hline \end{array}$$

$44 + 33 =$

$$\begin{array}{r} \\ + \\ \hline \end{array}$$

⑤ **Write the answers.**

$$\begin{array}{r} 2 \\ +5 \\ \hline \end{array} \quad \begin{array}{r} 7 \\ +6 \\ \hline \end{array} \quad \begin{array}{r} 0 \\ +3 \\ \hline \end{array} \quad \begin{array}{r} 6 \\ +5 \\ \hline \end{array} \quad \begin{array}{r} 2 \\ +8 \\ \hline \end{array} \quad \begin{array}{r} 1 \\ +2 \\ \hline \end{array}$$

$$\begin{array}{r} 9 \\ +7 \\ \hline \end{array} \quad \begin{array}{r} 5 \\ +4 \\ \hline \end{array}$$

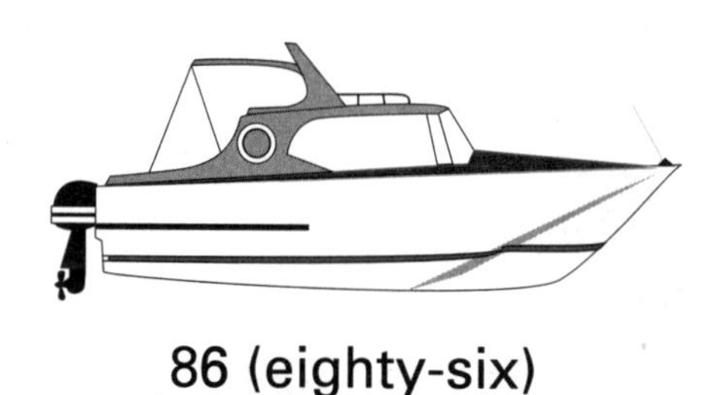

$$\begin{array}{r} 0 \\ +7 \\ \hline \end{array} \quad \begin{array}{r} 3 \\ +4 \\ \hline \end{array}$$

TEST 4

① Write the correct time. 4 pts. total for this exercise.

____:____ ____:____ ____:____ ____:____

② Draw a line to match the coin to cents. 6 pts.

5¢

1¢

10¢

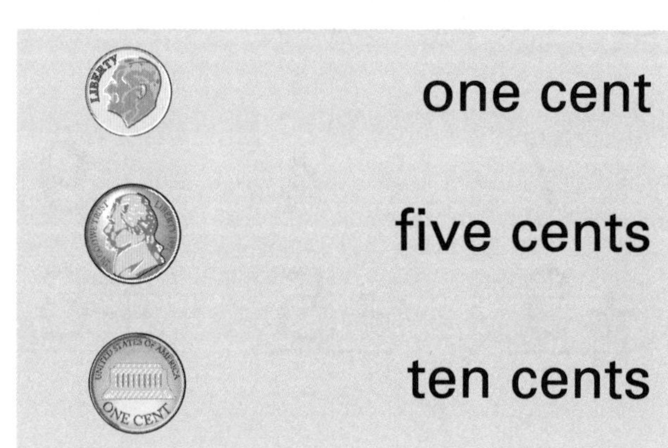

③ Write the number that comes before. 12 pts.

___ 32	___ 60	___ 28	___ 74
___ 16	___ 55	___ 8	___ 47
___ 81	___ 39	___ 93	___ 66

④ Measure the objects using the ruler. 2 pts.

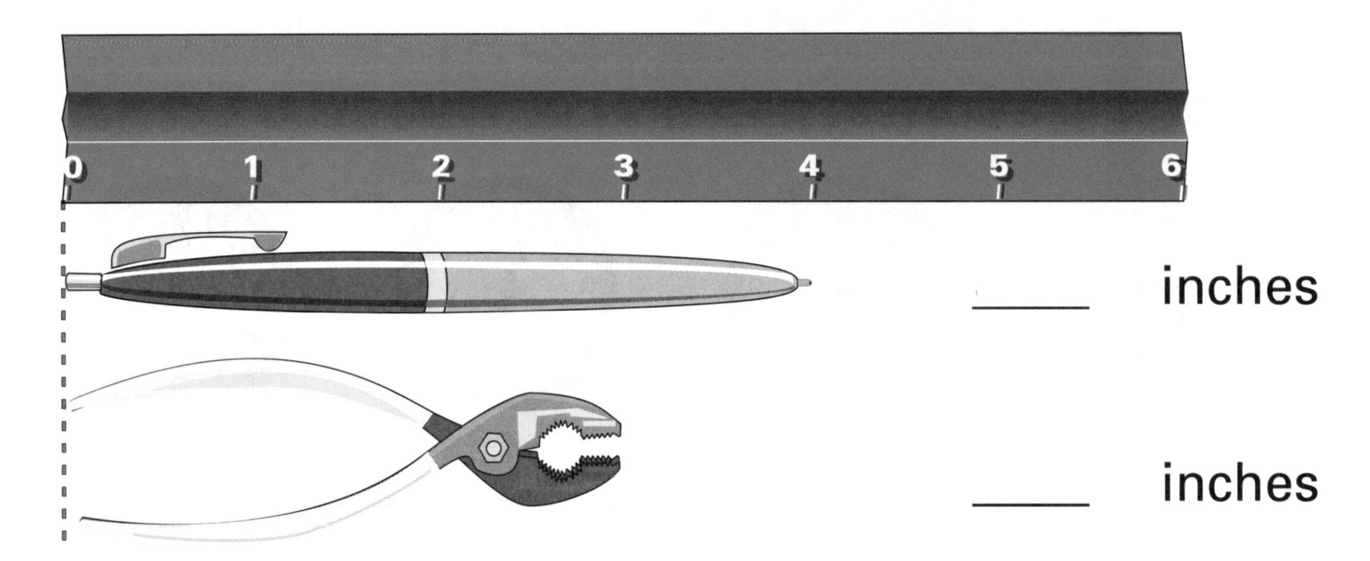

____ inches

____ inches

⑤ Write the answers. 16 pts. total for this exercise.

$$\begin{array}{r} 7 \\ +9 \\ \hline \end{array} \quad \begin{array}{r} 4 \\ +5 \\ \hline \end{array} \quad \begin{array}{r} 9 \\ +6 \\ \hline \end{array} \quad \begin{array}{r} 3 \\ +2 \\ \hline \end{array} \quad \begin{array}{r} 8 \\ +9 \\ \hline \end{array} \quad \begin{array}{r} 3 \\ +4 \\ \hline \end{array}$$

$$\begin{array}{r} 2 \\ +9 \\ \hline \end{array} \quad \begin{array}{r} 5 \\ +3 \\ \hline \end{array} \quad \begin{array}{r} 8 \\ +6 \\ \hline \end{array} \quad \begin{array}{r} 6 \\ +1 \\ \hline \end{array} \quad \begin{array}{r} 9 \\ +2 \\ \hline \end{array} \quad \begin{array}{r} 9 \\ +7 \\ \hline \end{array}$$

$$\begin{array}{r} 0 \\ +8 \\ \hline \end{array} \quad \begin{array}{r} 7 \\ +8 \\ \hline \end{array} \quad \begin{array}{r} 6 \\ +7 \\ \hline \end{array} \quad \begin{array}{r} 4 \\ +3 \\ \hline \end{array}$$

40 pts. Total

CALENDAR – DAYS OF THE WEEK

1 Write the missing numbers.

November

Sunday	Monday	Tuesday	Wednesday	Thursday	Friday	Saturday
					1	2
3				7		
	11		13			16
17					22	
		26				30

The calendar is for what month? ____________

What is the date on the first Monday? ____________

What is the date on the last Sunday? ____________

What is the date on the fourth Friday? ____________

How many days are in a week? ____________

How many Tuesdays are in November? ____________

② Write the problems vertically. Write the answers.

$19 + 30 =$

$46 + 41 =$

$31 + 52 =$

$29 + 40 =$

③ Write the answers.

8 +3	7 +6	4 +7	6 +8	5 +9	6 +4
1 +9	9 +9	9 +4	8 +7	8 +5	9 +1
3 +9	4 +8			2 +8	7 +5

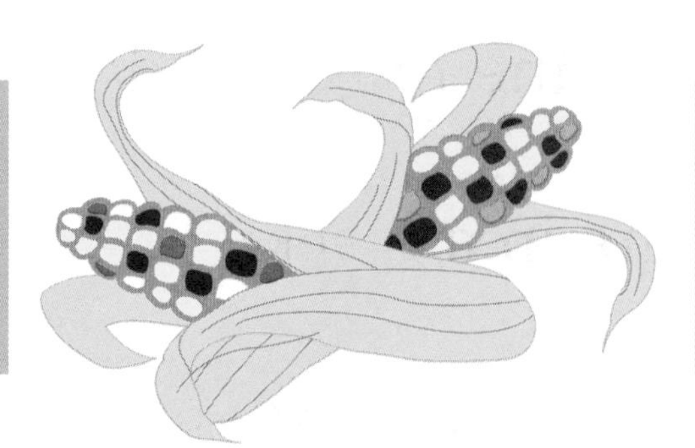

SHOW YOUR SKILLS

① **Write = or ≠ between each set.**

five____ 4
3+3____ 5
5+2____ 7
10¢____ dime
5¢____ nickel

eight ____ 7
3+8 ____ 10
6+3 ____ 9
20¢ ____ 2 nickels
30¢ ____ 3 dimes

② **Write the number that comes before and after.**

___	49	___	___	68	___	___	15	___
___	81	___	___	6	___	___	32	___
___	24	___	___	73	___	___	57	___

③ **Circle the correct answer.**

What is the first day of the week?
Saturday Friday Sunday

What is the last day of the week?
Saturday Friday Sunday

④ Brad caught 5 fish. David caught 6 fish. How many fish did they catch altogether?

____ + ____ = ____ fish

Wade has 3 library books to return to the library. Beth gave him 6 to return for her. How many library books did Wade return altogether?

____ + ____ = ____ books

Science Experiments History Adventures Bible Stories

⑤ **Write the answers.**

6 +5	7 +8	3 +8	3 +6	5 +5	6 +7
6 +9	8 +7	5 +8	6 +5	0 +9	12 + 0
72 +20	45 +30	53 +24	32 +24	77 +11	60 +35

TIME – QUARTER HOUR

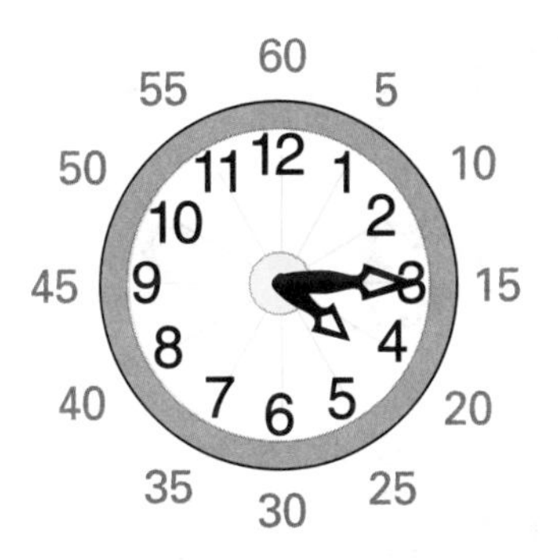

The long hand is on the 3 at 4:15.

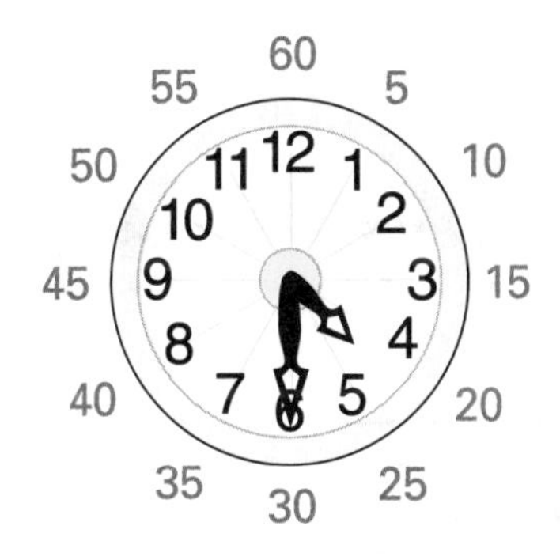

The long hand is on the 6 at 4:30.

The long hand is on the 9 at 4:45.

1 **Write the correct time.**

___:___

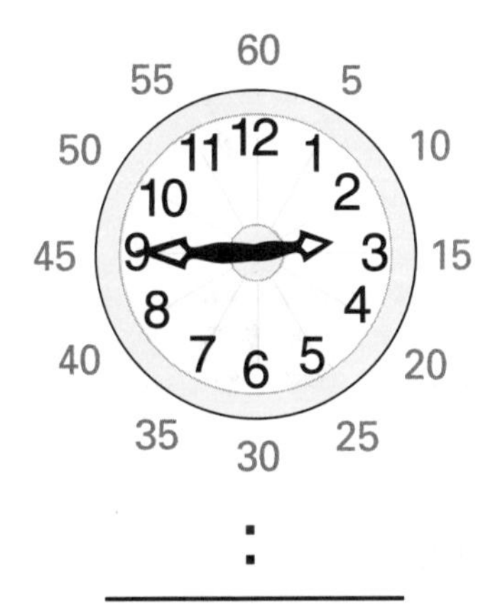

___:___

___:___

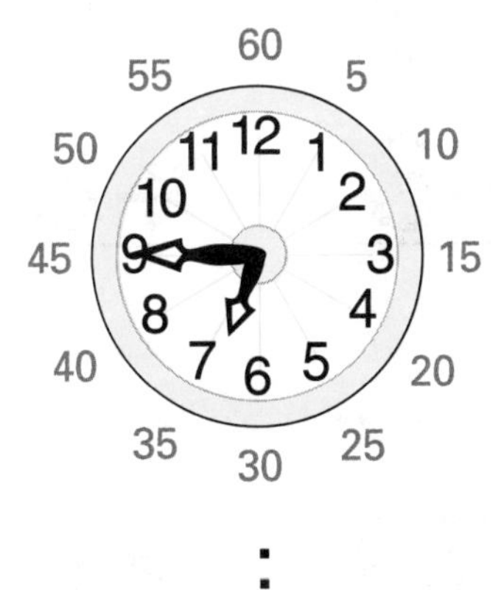

___:___

___:___

___:___

② **Write = or ≠ between each set.**

8+3 ___ 12	7+5 ___ 12	3+9 ___ 12
4+2 ___ 5	6+7 ___ 14	2+3 ___ 3+2
6+4 ___ 10	7+6 ___ 14	8+5 ___ 13

③ **Write the number that comes before and after.**

___ 24 ___	___ 60 ___	___ 82 ___
___ 59 ___	___ 7 ___	___ 93 ___
___ 41 ___	___ 36 ___	___ 18 ___

④ **Write the answers.**

6	7	5	3	3	5
+5	+8	+5	+7	+8	+8

27	42			73	80
+42	+51			+25	+12

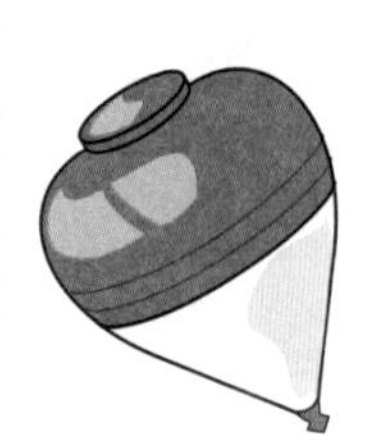
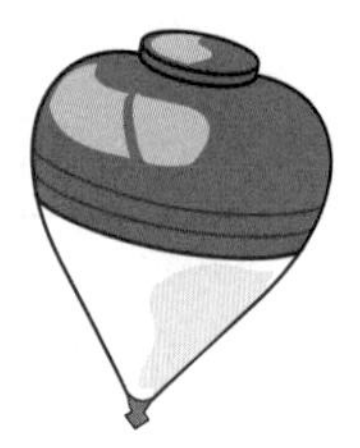

MONEY – PENNIES AND DIMES

① **Circle the dimes and pennies needed.**

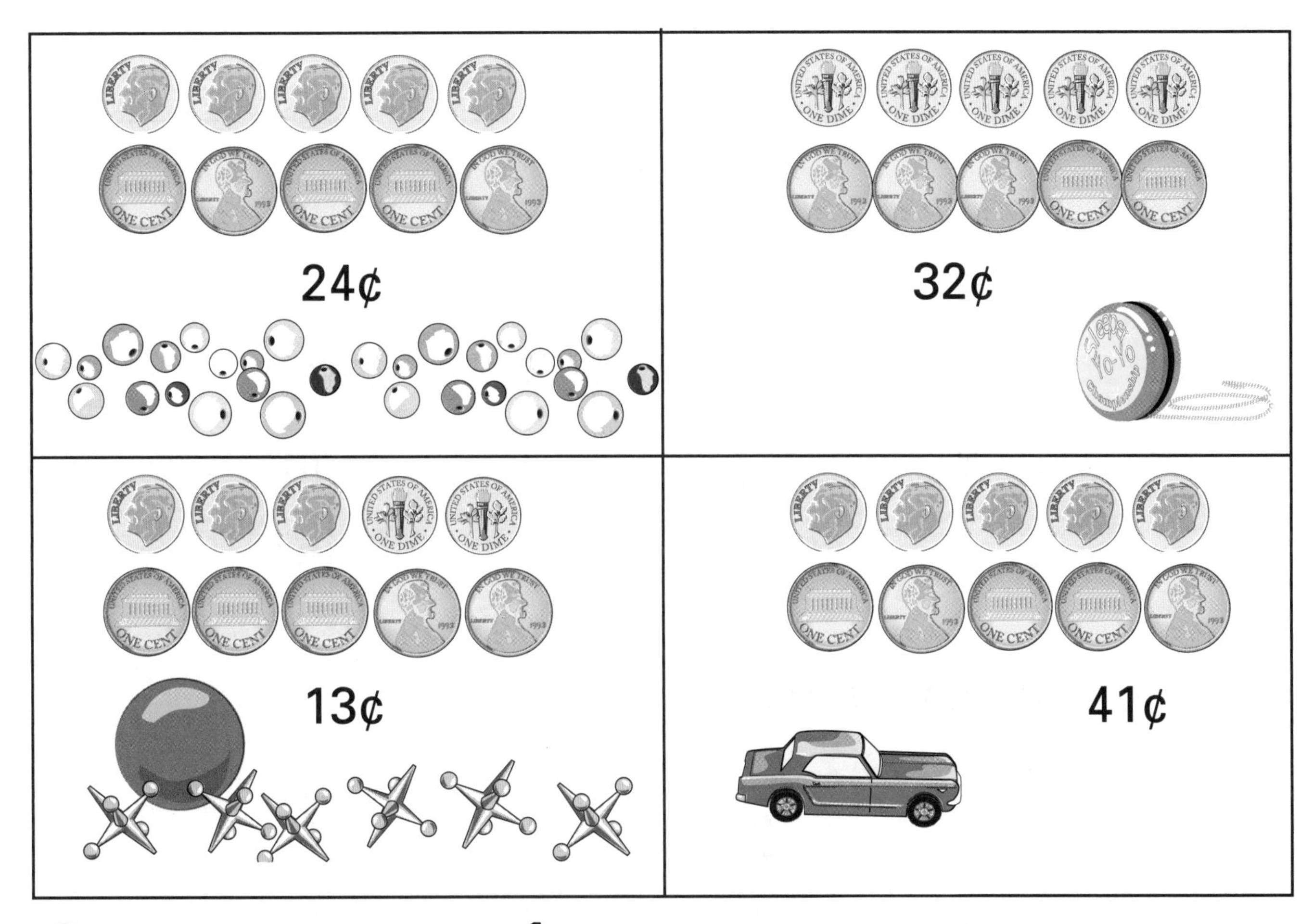

② **Color one half ($\frac{1}{2}$) of each object.**

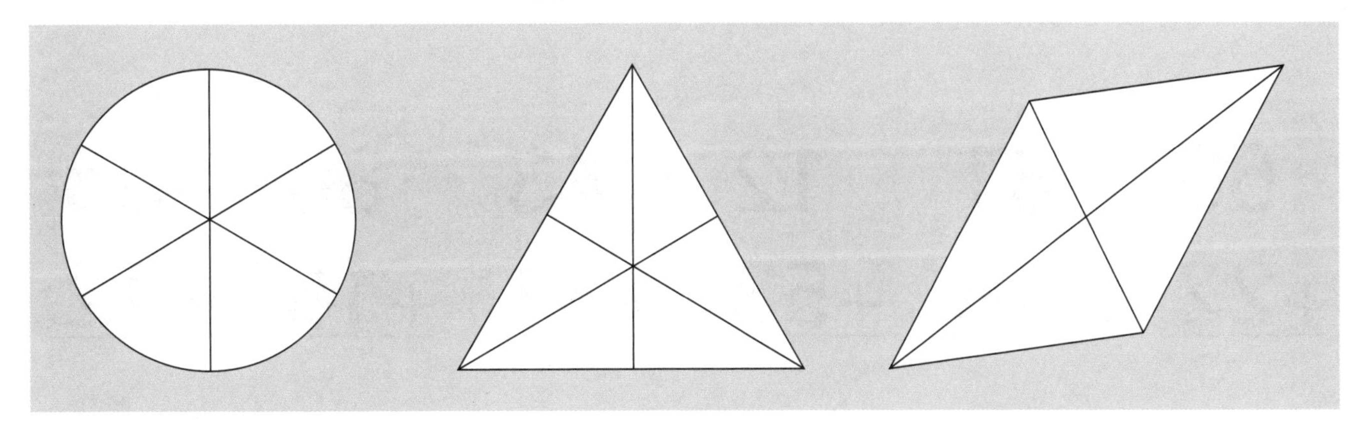

③ Write the correct time.

___:___	___:___	___:___	___:___

④ Write < or > between each set.

seven _____ 8	4 + 6 _____ 9	three _____ 30
ten _____ 8	7 + 5 _____ 10	eight _____ 9
four _____ 3	3 + 4 _____ 8	nine _____ 6

⑤ Write the answers.

6	3	5	4	7	8
+9	+8	+7	+6	+4	+5

66	61	12	43	80	33
+22	+18	+53	+31	+16	+12

NUMBER ORDER – BEFORE AND AFTER BY 10

1 **When counting by 10's, write the number that comes before and after.**

___ 20 ___	___ 50 ___	___ 80 ___
___ 40 ___	___ 70 ___	___ 60 ___
___ 10 ___	___ 90 ___	___ 30 ___

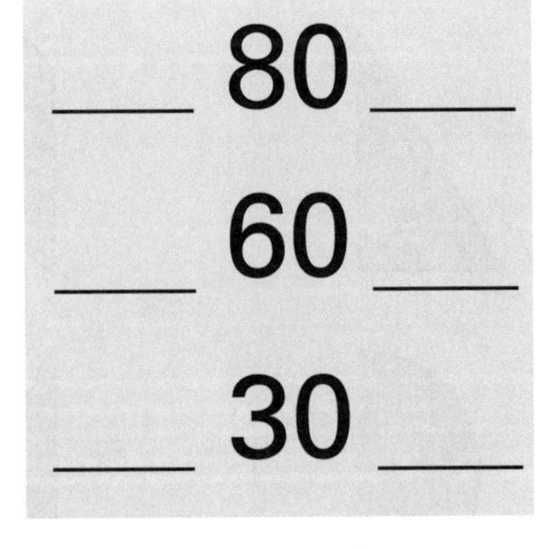

2 **Draw a line to match the clock with the time.**

5:15 8:00 2:45 10:15

3 **Write < or > between each set.**

5+6 ___ 10	9+7 ___ 15	8+3 ___ 14
4+7 ___ 14	6+8 ___ 12	9+6 ___ 16
2+9 ___ 10	7+7 ___ 15	3+9 ___ 11

4 **Draw a line to match one half to the other.**

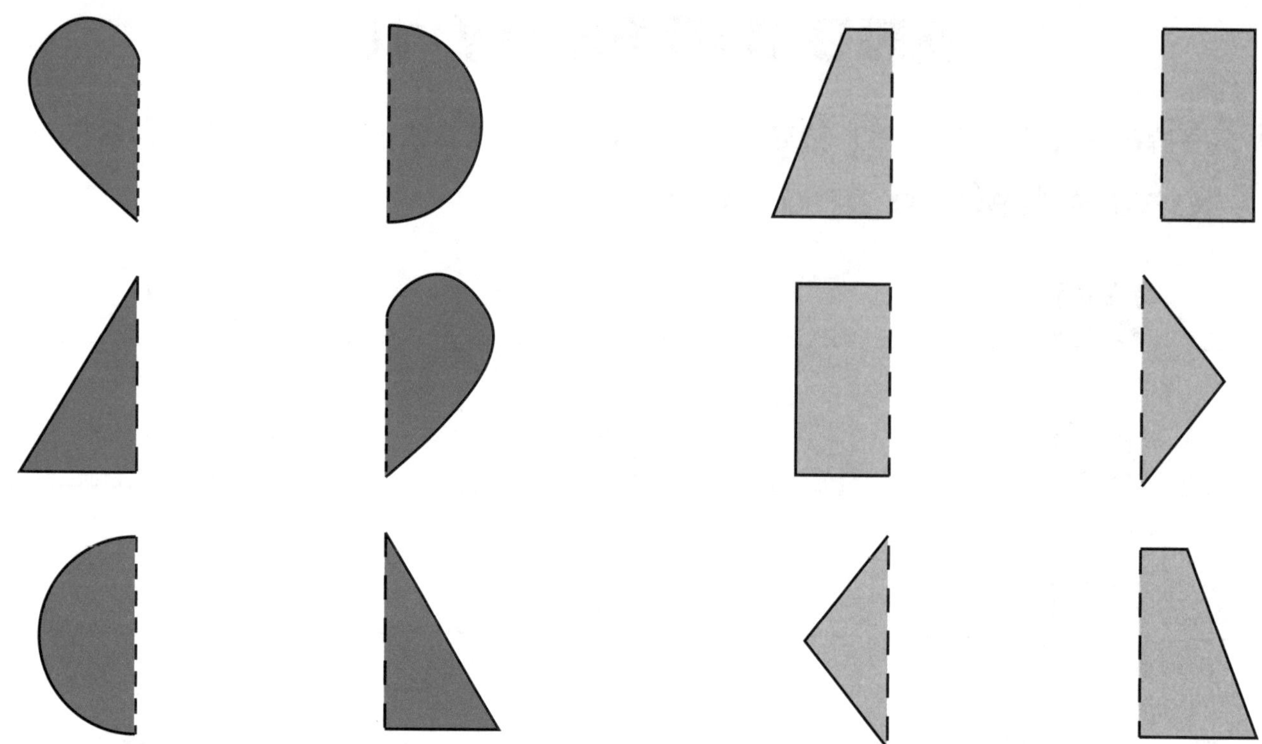

5 Mother baked 4 loaves of bread on Monday. She baked 6 more on Wednesday. Altogether Mother baked how many loaves of bread?

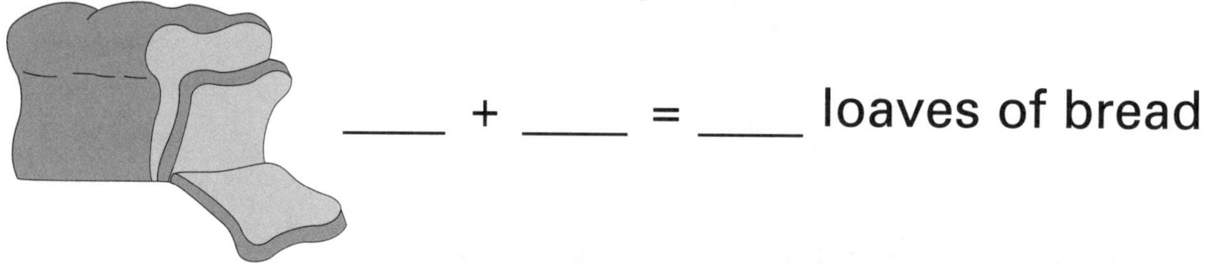

____ + ____ = ____ loaves of bread

Barb painted 5 pictures in art class. Tye painted 9 pictures at home. How many pictures did they paint altogether?

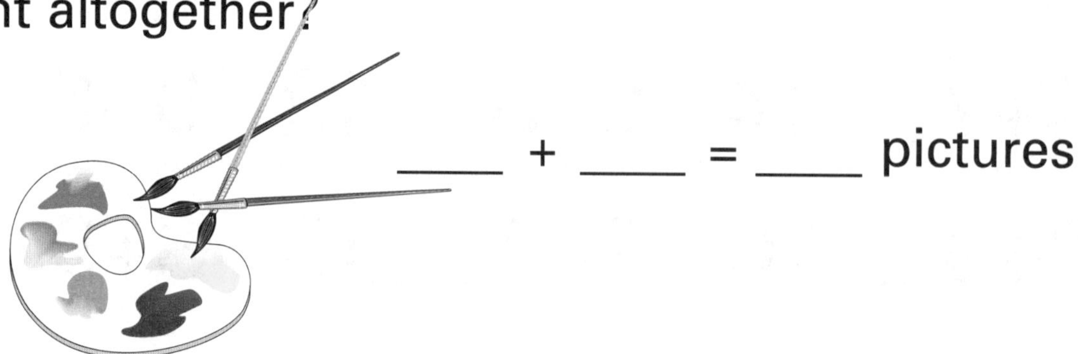

____ + ____ = ____ pictures

ADDITION – THREE NUMBERS

① **Add the numbers.**

3
2 add 3+2= 5
+1 → +1
6

2
2 add 2+2= ___
+5 → +5

1
2 add 1+2= ___
+2 → +2

4
1 add 4+1= ___
+3 → +3

4 3 +1 8 (4+3=7)	1 6 +2	3 1 +2	4 2 +2	7 2 +1	5 3 +2

② **Draw the short (hour) hand on the clock.**

12:15 8:30 1:45 5:15

③ **Measure each object with a ruler.**

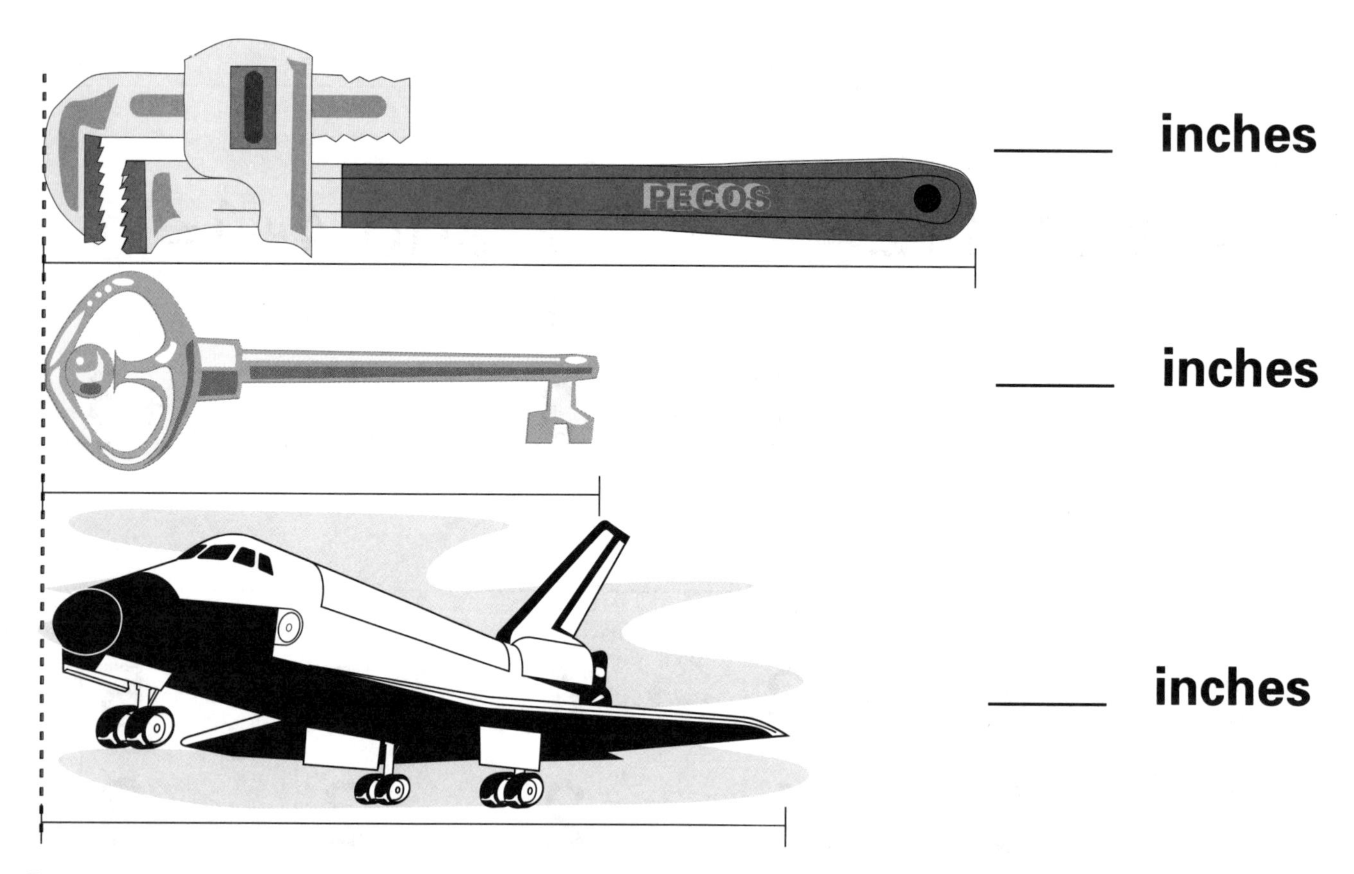

____ **inches**

____ **inches**

____ **inches**

④ Chad had 8 dimes in his left pocket and 6 dimes in his right pocket. Chad had how many dimes altogether? Write the addition fact and label the answer.

____ + ____ = ____ ______________

SHOW YOUR SKILLS

① Write the answers in the blanks.

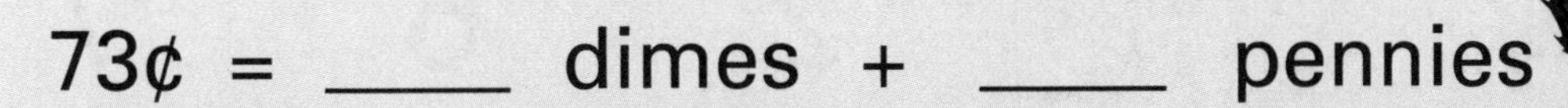

73¢ = ____ dimes + ____ pennies

27¢ = ____ dimes + ____ pennies

56¢ = ____ dimes + ____ pennies

14¢ = ____ dime + ____ pennies

② Measure the lines with an inch ruler. Write the answer.

____ inches

____ inches

____ inches

____ inches

③ When counting by 10's, write the number that comes before and after.

____ 90 ____ ____ 30 ____ ____ 10 ____

____ 20 ____ ____ 50 ____ ____ 40 ____

④ **Write the answers.**

$$\begin{array}{r} 2 \\ 4 \\ +1 \\ \hline \end{array} \quad \begin{array}{r} 2 \\ 5 \\ +3 \\ \hline \end{array} \quad \begin{array}{r} 1 \\ 2 \\ +7 \\ \hline \end{array} \quad \begin{array}{r} 2 \\ 7 \\ +4 \\ \hline \end{array} \quad \begin{array}{r} 6 \\ 2 \\ +3 \\ \hline \end{array} \quad \begin{array}{r} 7 \\ 2 \\ +9 \\ \hline \end{array}$$

$$\begin{array}{r} 3 \\ +8 \\ \hline \end{array} \quad \begin{array}{r} 5 \\ +9 \\ \hline \end{array} \quad \begin{array}{r} 4 \\ +7 \\ \hline \end{array} \quad \begin{array}{r} 7 \\ +3 \\ \hline \end{array} \quad \begin{array}{r} 8 \\ +2 \\ \hline \end{array} \quad \begin{array}{r} 6 \\ +7 \\ \hline \end{array}$$

$$\begin{array}{r} 82 \\ +17 \\ \hline \end{array} \quad \begin{array}{r} 14 \\ +72 \\ \hline \end{array} \quad \begin{array}{r} 25 \\ +50 \\ \hline \end{array} \quad \begin{array}{r} 72 \\ +17 \\ \hline \end{array} \quad \begin{array}{r} 36 \\ +43 \\ \hline \end{array} \quad \begin{array}{r} 20 \\ +35 \\ \hline \end{array}$$

⑤ Chuck gave Shawn 2 donuts. Shawn already had 7 donuts. Shawn had how many donuts altogether? Write the addition fact and label the answer.

____ + ____ = ____ ________________

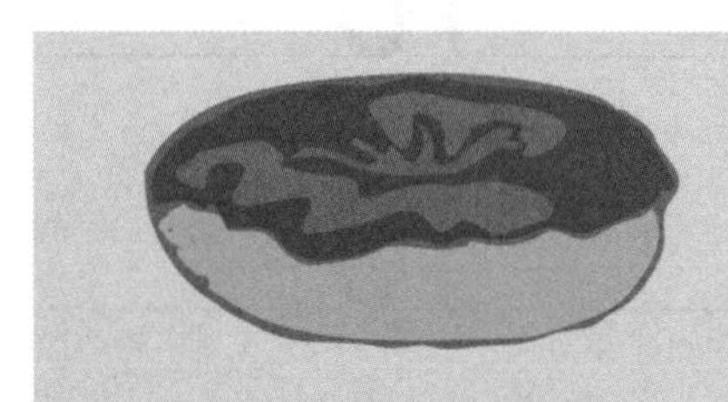

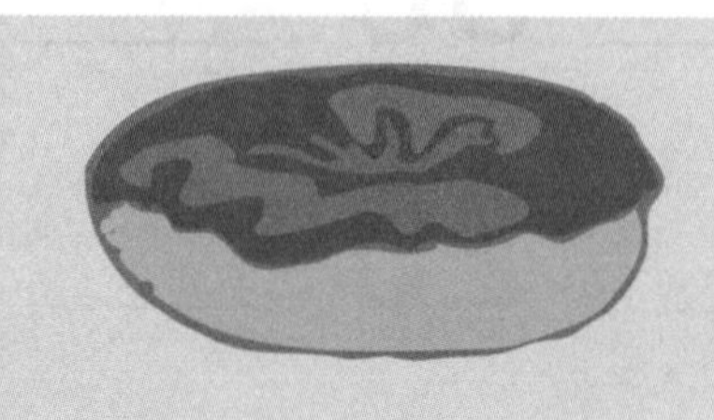

WORD NUMBERS – ELEVEN TO TWENTY

① **Draw a line to match the word number and number.**

11	twelve	20	forty
12	fourteen	30	twenty
13	eleven	40	fifty
14	fifteen	50	thirty
15	thirteen	60	eighty
16	eighteen	70	sixty
17	seventeen	80	one hundred
18	sixteen	90	seventy
19	nineteen	100	ninety

② **Draw a line with the ruler.**

2 inches

•

5 inches

•

3 inches

•

4 inches

•

3 **Draw the pennies and dimes needed.**

23¢ ____________________

41¢ ____________________

16¢ ____________________

34¢ ____________________

4 Ron read 10 pages on Tuesday and 8 pages on Wednesday. How many pages did Ron read altogether? Write the addition fact and label the answer.

____ + ____ = ____ ______________

5 **Write the answers.**

$$\begin{array}{r}5\\3\\+7\\\hline\end{array}\quad\begin{array}{r}4\\4\\+9\\\hline\end{array}\quad\begin{array}{r}2\\6\\+4\\\hline\end{array}\quad\begin{array}{r}3\\3\\+8\\\hline\end{array}\quad\begin{array}{r}1\\5\\+9\\\hline\end{array}\quad\begin{array}{r}5\\4\\+7\\\hline\end{array}$$

$$\begin{array}{r}36\\+23\\\hline\end{array}\quad\begin{array}{r}25\\+41\\\hline\end{array}\quad\begin{array}{r}76\\+20\\\hline\end{array}\quad\begin{array}{r}22\\+44\\\hline\end{array}$$

MONEY – NICKELS

① **Count the nickels by 5's. Circle the correct cents.**

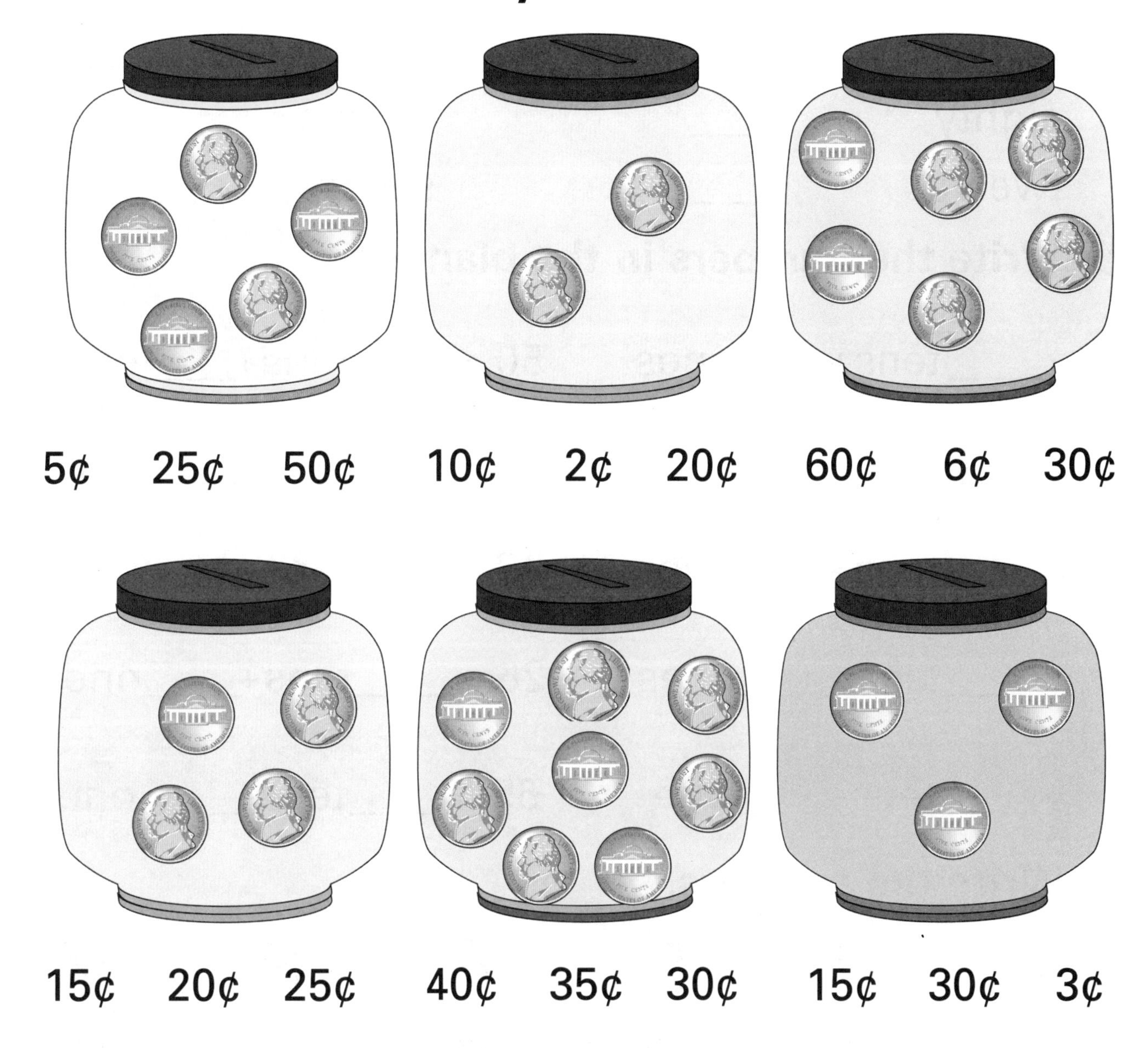

5¢ 25¢ 50¢ | 10¢ 2¢ 20¢ | 60¢ 6¢ 30¢

15¢ 20¢ 25¢ | 40¢ 35¢ 30¢ | 15¢ 30¢ 3¢

② Joy has 4 kittens. Faith's cat had 6 new baby kittens. How many kittens do Joy and Faith have altogether? Write the addition fact and label the answer.

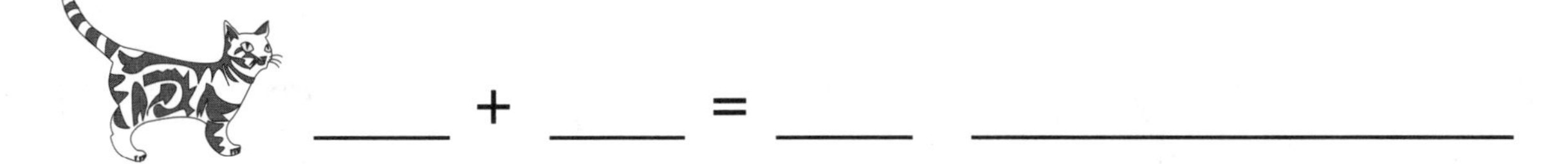

____ + ____ = ____ ________________

③ **Write the number in the blank.**

thirteen	_____	fifteen	_____
nineteen	_____	sixty	_____
forty	_____	twenty	_____
eighty	_____	eleven	_____
twelve	_____	seventy	_____

④ **Write the numbers in the blanks.**

72 =_____tens+_____ones	50 =_____tens+_____ones
54 =_____tens+_____ones	17 =_____ten +_____ones
8 =_____tens+_____ones	43 =_____tens+_____ones
39 =_____tens+_____ones	26 =_____tens+_____ones
81 =_____tens+_____one	65 =_____tens+_____ones

⑤ **Write the answers.**

$\begin{array}{r} 2 \\ +9 \\ \hline \end{array}$ $\begin{array}{r} 4 \\ +6 \\ \hline \end{array}$ $\begin{array}{r} 5 \\ +8 \\ \hline \end{array}$ $\begin{array}{r} 6 \\ +9 \\ \hline \end{array}$ $\begin{array}{r} 8 \\ +8 \\ \hline \end{array}$ $\begin{array}{r} 9 \\ +7 \\ \hline \end{array}$

$\begin{array}{r} 16 \\ +53 \\ \hline \end{array}$ $\begin{array}{r} 44 \\ +22 \\ \hline \end{array}$

$\begin{array}{r} 72 \\ +12 \\ \hline \end{array}$ $\begin{array}{r} 21 \\ +74 \\ \hline \end{array}$

FRACTIONS – ONE FOURTH

① Color one fourth ($\frac{1}{4}$) of each shape.

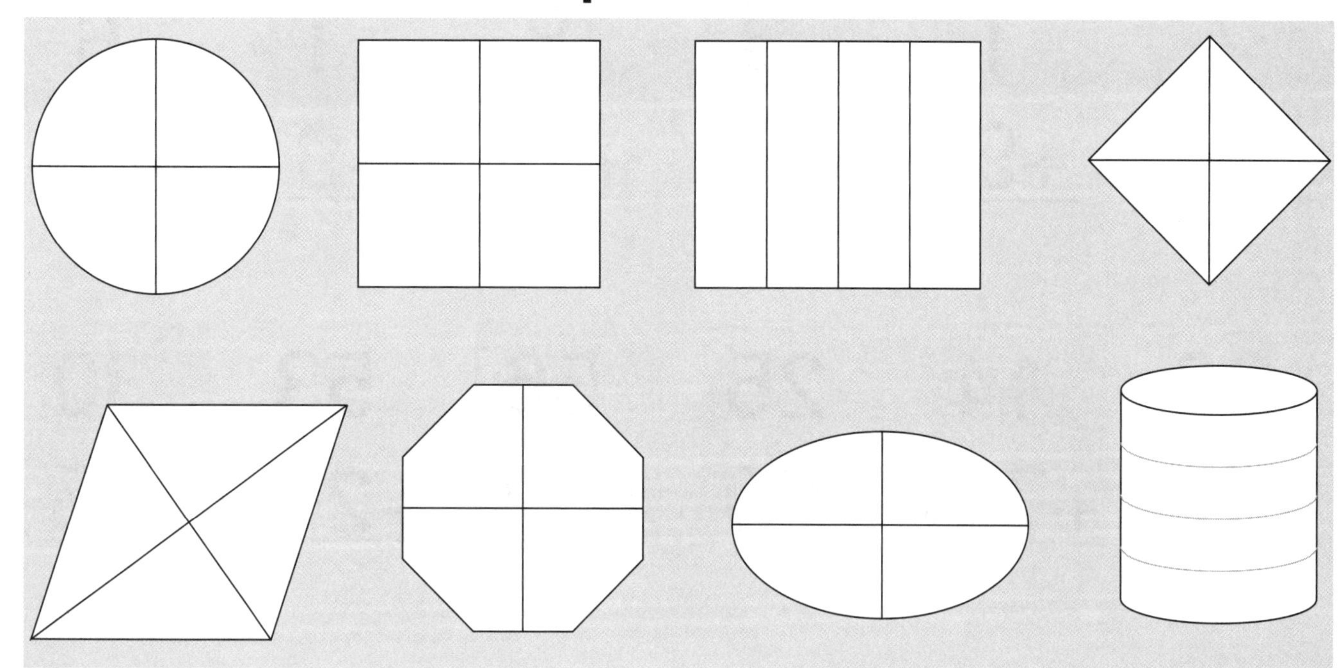

② Write the number.

5 tens = _____	8 tens = _____	2 tens = _____
6 tens = _____	4 tens = _____	9 tens = _____
1 ten = _____	7 tens = _____	3 tens = _____

③ Draw a line to match the nickels to cents.

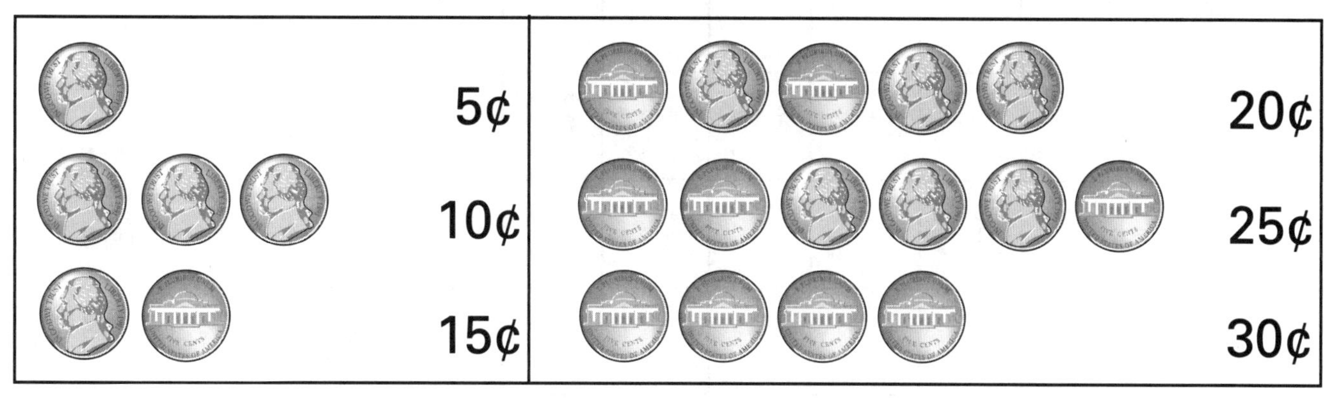

④ Write the answers.

2 4 +8	6 1 +9	4 3 +7	1 8 +7	5 1 +9	2 6 +9

82 +17	14 +72	25 +50	56 +32	53 +22	30 +35

32 +16	45 +51	74 +11	61 +38	24 +25	20 +73

⑤ Write the missing numbers.

50					55				
	61								
							77		
			83						
									99

TEST 5

① Write the correct time. 4 pts. total for this exercise.

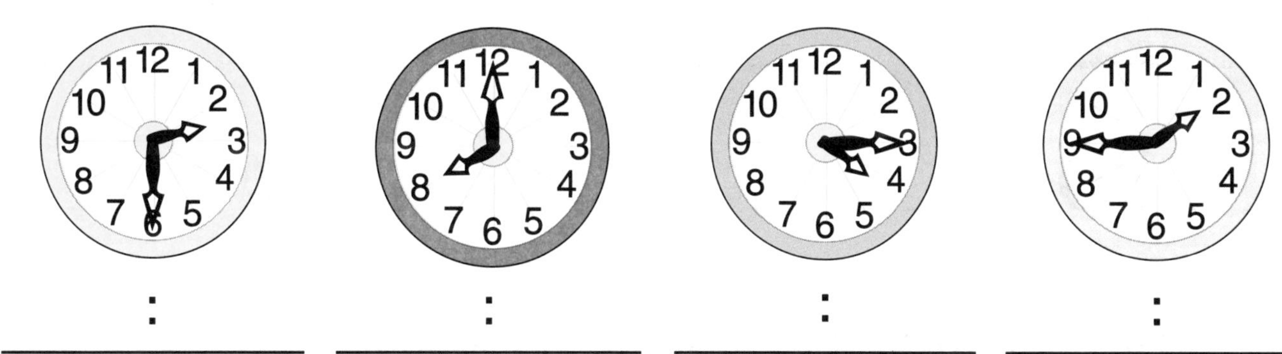

: : : :

② Write how many cents in each set. 5 pts.

____¢

____¢

____¢

____¢

____¢

③ Draw a line to divide each animal in half. 4 pts.

④ **Write the number that comes before and after.**
12 pts. total for this exercise.

___ 23 ___	___ 56 ___	___ 8 ___
___ 30 ___	___ 87 ___	___ 41 ___

⑤ **Write the answers.** **12 pts. total for this exercise.**

$$\begin{array}{r}3\\3\\+3\\\hline\end{array}\quad\begin{array}{r}6\\3\\+2\\\hline\end{array}\quad\begin{array}{r}5\\3\\+3\\\hline\end{array}\quad\begin{array}{r}8\\1\\+5\\\hline\end{array}\quad\begin{array}{r}7\\1\\+1\\\hline\end{array}\quad\begin{array}{r}7\\0\\+2\\\hline\end{array}$$

$$\begin{array}{r}16\\+53\\\hline\end{array}\quad\begin{array}{r}44\\+22\\\hline\end{array}\quad\begin{array}{r}72\\+12\\\hline\end{array}\quad\begin{array}{r}21\\+74\\\hline\end{array}\quad\begin{array}{r}54\\+25\\\hline\end{array}\quad\begin{array}{r}10\\+33\\\hline\end{array}$$

⑥ Amy brought 4 dimes for lunch. Anita brought 6 dimes. Amy and Anita had how many dimes altogether? Write the addition fact and label the answer. **4 pts.**

____ + ____ = ____ ________________

41 pts. Total

SHOW YOUR SKILLS

① **Draw the objects.**

big tree　　little tree　　big man　　little man

② **Draw lines to divide each object into 4 equal pieces. Shade one fourth ($\frac{1}{4}$) of each object.**

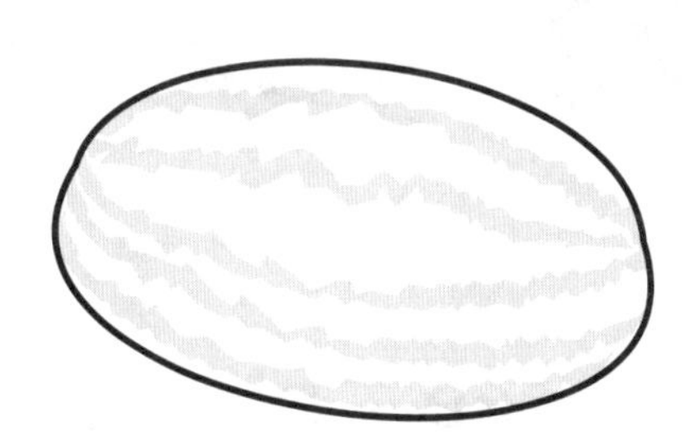

③ **Write the missing numbers when counting by 10's.**

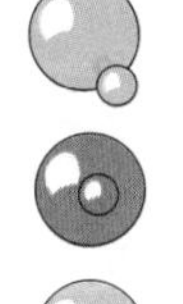

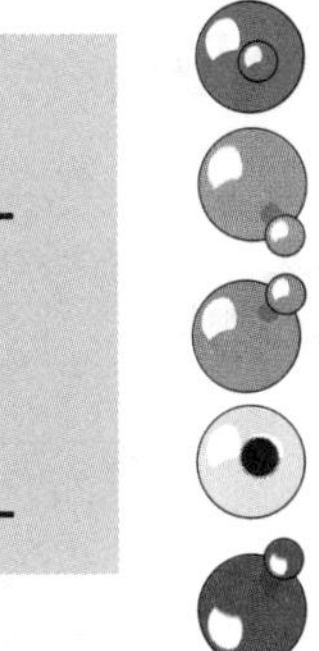

10　____　____　40　____

____　70　____　____　____

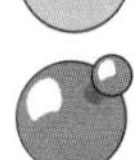

④ **Write the answers.**

1 8 +4	5 5 +3	9 1 +0	1 6 +5	3 2 +5	2 4 +1

14 +72	56 +32	63 +35	65 +23	53 +16	15 +20

70 +22	63 +23	14 +34	81 +16	82 +15	46 +23

⑤ Sam could see 7 blue birds in his tree. Across the road he could see 9 black birds on the fence. Sam could see how many birds altogether? Write the addition fact and label the answer.

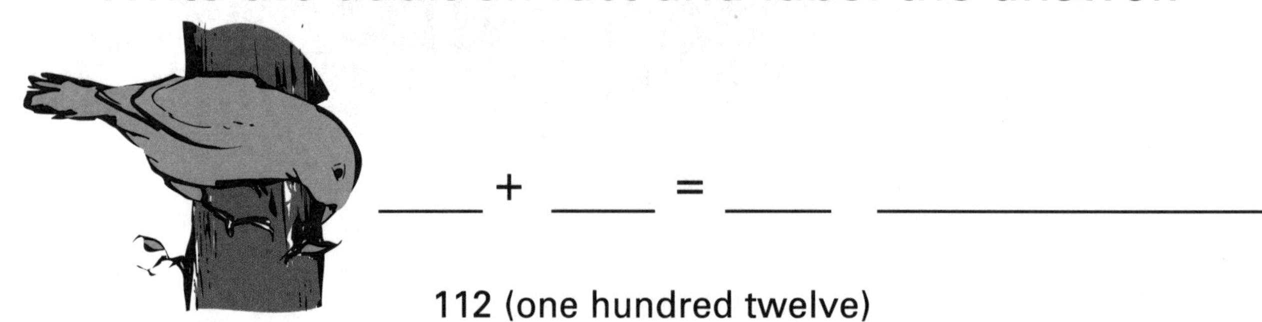

____ + ____ = ____ ________________

MONEY – QUARTER

25 cents

25¢

1 **Count the quarters by 25's.**

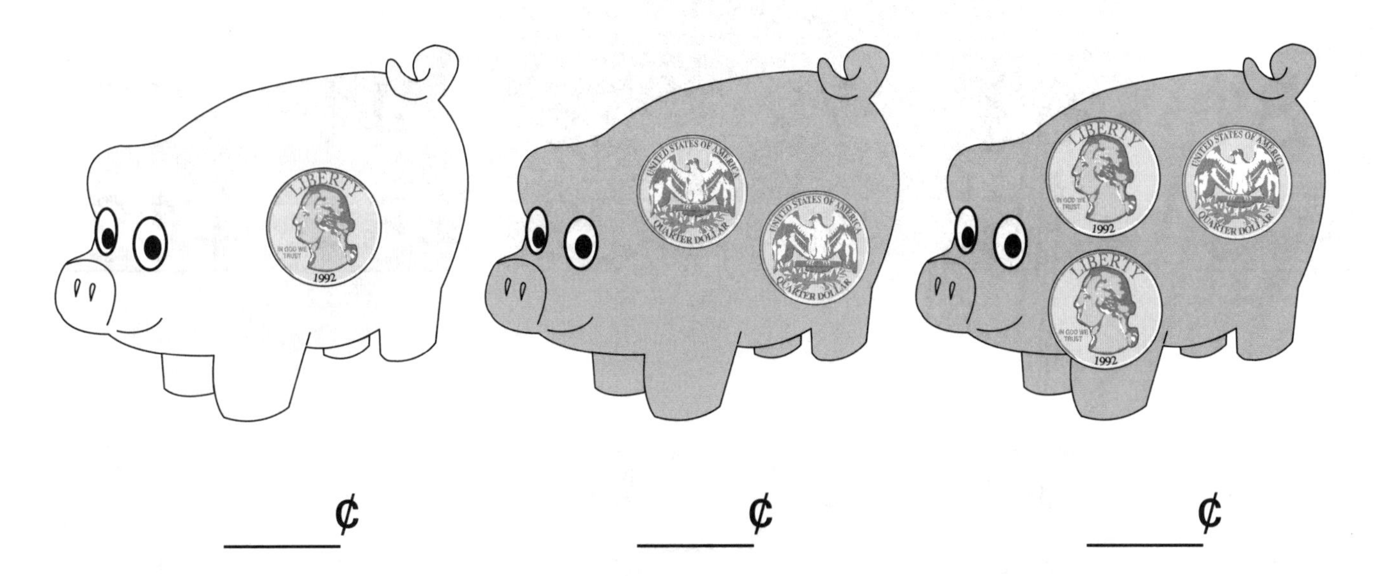

_____¢ _____¢ _____¢

2 **Write = or ≠ between each set.**

3 dimes	_____	30¢	4 nickels	_____	20¢
7 pennies	_____	7¢	1 quarter	_____	75¢
2 dimes and 3 pennies	_____	32¢	5 dimes	_____	25¢

③ **Color $\frac{1}{4}$ of the objects divided into 4 parts.**

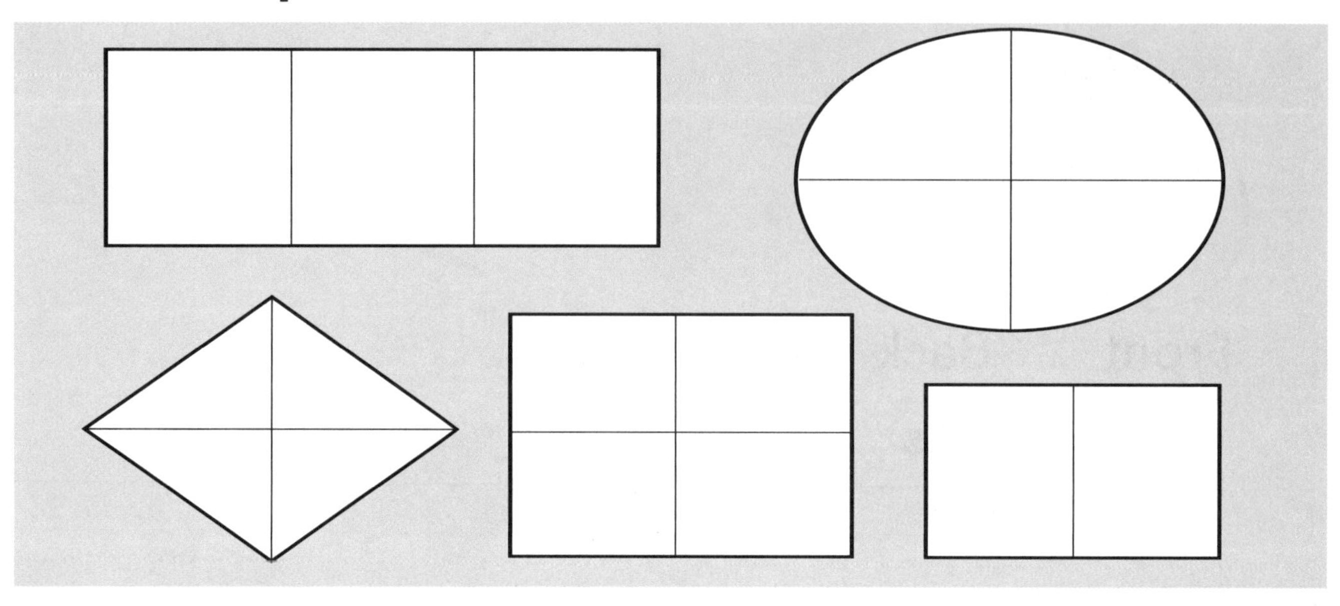

④ **Write the answers.**

81	63	72	25	41	22
+15	+35	+14	+32	+54	+12

37	33	63	60	22	44
+42	+44	+15	+29	+57	+10

⑤ Ron bought a drink with 7 nickels and a candy bar with 4 nickels. How many nickels did Ron need altogether? Write the addition fact and label the answer.

_____ + _____ = _____ ____________________

SUBTRACTION

① **Write the answers.**

7-3=4

$$\begin{array}{r} 7 \\ -\ 3 \\ \hline 4 \end{array}$$

5-2=3

$$\begin{array}{r} 5 \\ -\ 2 \\ \hline 3 \end{array}$$

7-1=___

$$\begin{array}{r} 7 \\ -\ 1 \\ \hline \end{array}$$

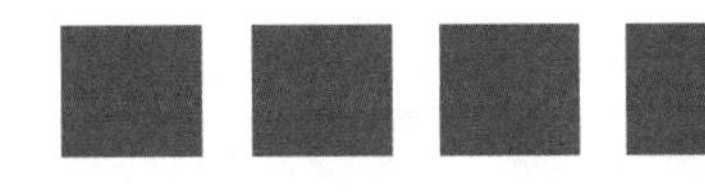

6-2=___

$$\begin{array}{r} 6 \\ -\ 2 \\ \hline \end{array}$$

② **Write the value.**

___ ___ ___

_____¢

___ ___

_____¢

___

_____¢

③ **Write the fraction that shows what part is shaded.**

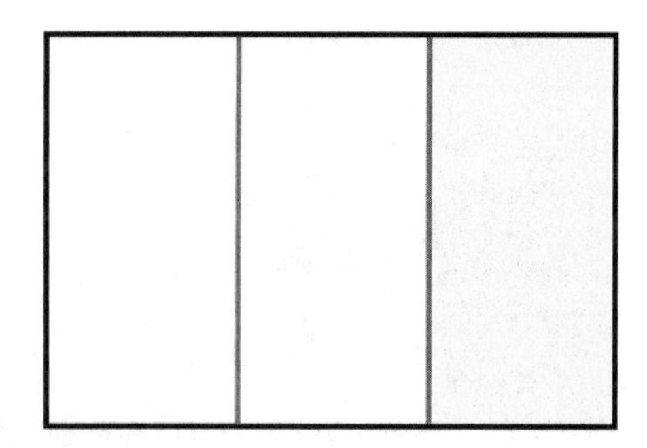

_____

_____

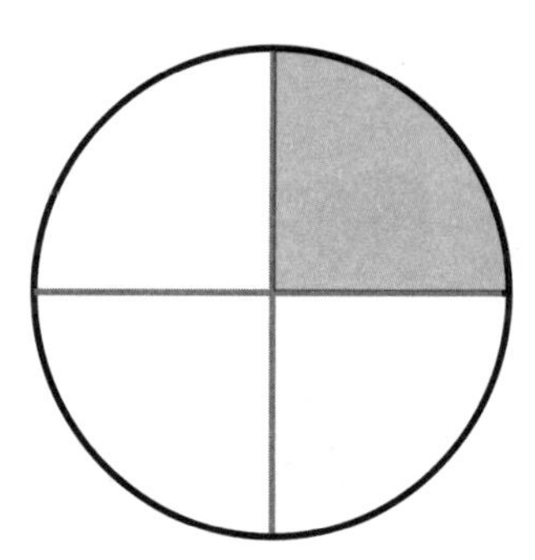

_____

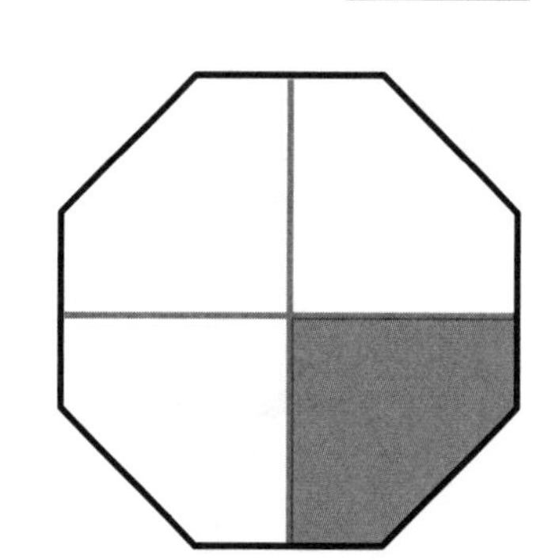

_____

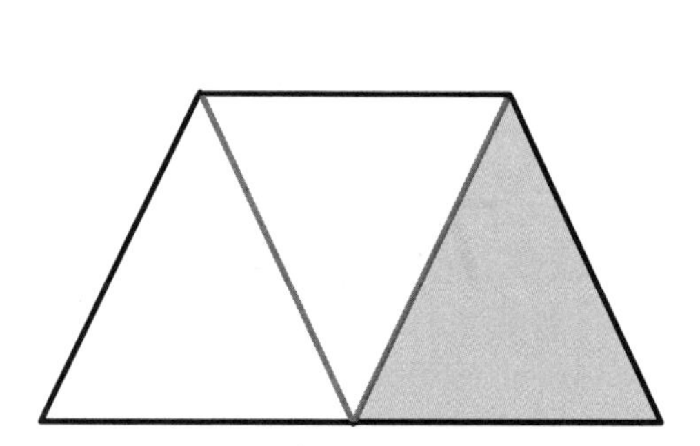

_____

④ **Write = or ≠ between each set.**

7+8 _____ 15   9+4 _____ 14   5+4 _____ 9

7+5 _____ 13   6+9 _____ 17   8+5 _____ 13

NUMBER ORDER – < AND >

① **Write < or > in the blanks.**

18 _____ sixteen	four _____ 8	16 _____ twenty
6 _____ fourteen	fifty _____ 36	71 _____ thirty
14 _____ twelve	forty _____ 26	6 _____ eleven
67 _____ eighty	thirty _____ 21	23 _____ nineteen

② **Color $\frac{1}{4}$** **Color $\frac{1}{2}$** **Color $\frac{1}{2}$**

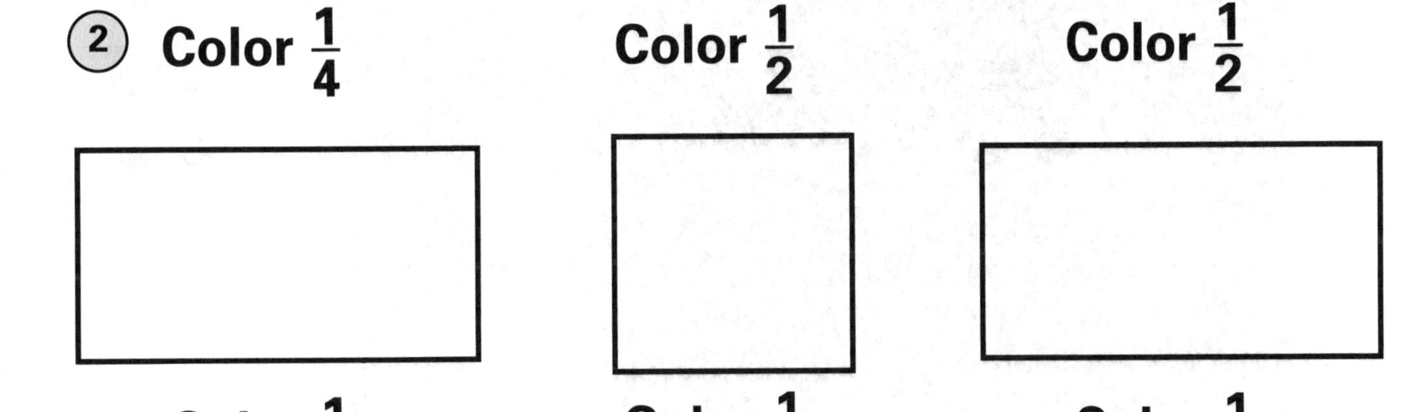

Color $\frac{1}{2}$ **Color $\frac{1}{4}$** **Color $\frac{1}{4}$**

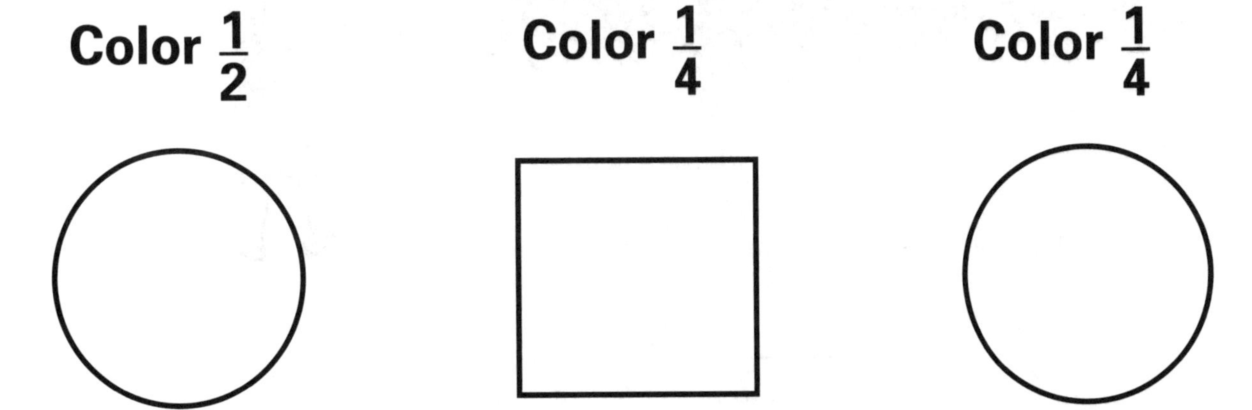

③ Lee had 5 baseball cards. Gene gave him 9 more cards. How many baseball cards does Lee now have? Label the answer.

_____ + _____ = _____ ____________________

④ Write the answers.

____ - ____ = ____

____ - ____ = ____ ____ - ____ = ____

____ - ____ = ____

⑤ Circle the correct answer.

10¢ 25¢ 50¢

25¢ 50¢ 75¢

5¢ 10¢ 25¢

TIME – HOUR AND HALF HOUR

1 Write the correct time.

:

:

:

:

:

:

:

:

:

:

:

:

2 If divided into 4 parts, color $\frac{1}{4}$.

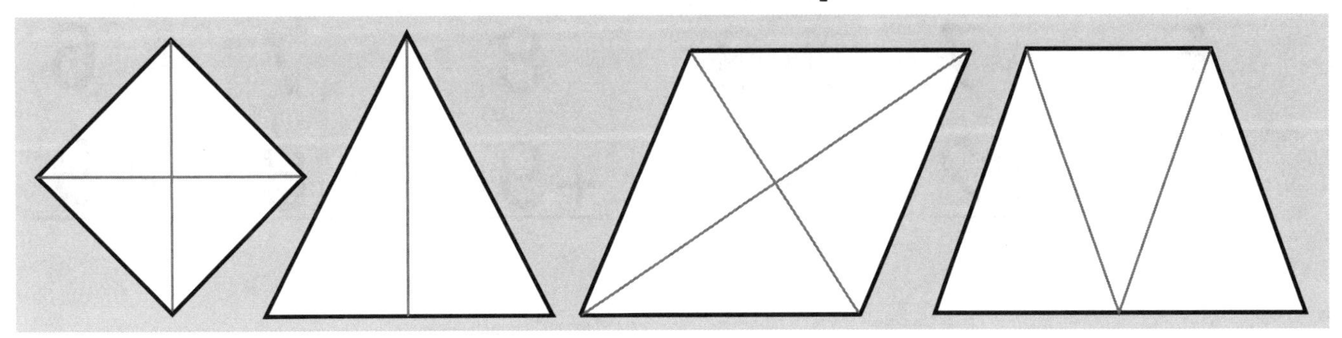

③ Write the answers.

___ - ___ = ___

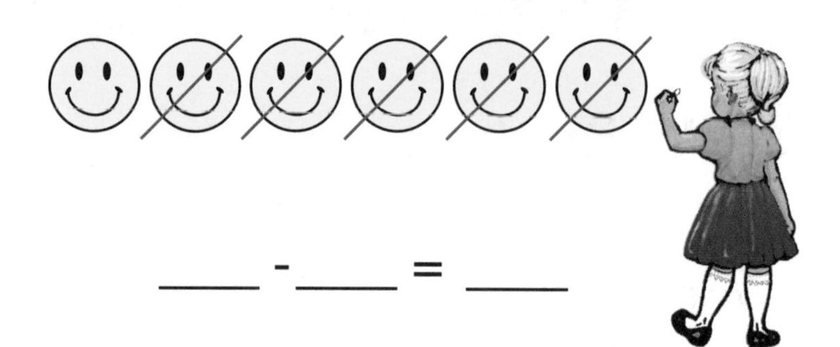

___ - ___ = ___

___ - ___ = ___   ___ - ___ = ___

④ Write < or > between each set.

6+5 ___ 10	7+4 ___ 12	8+9 ___ 10
8+2 ___ 17	9+9 ___ 34	2+3 ___ 0

⑤ Write the answers.

1	3	6	1	0	2
5	7	3	8	7	6
+8	+2	+4	+9	+8	+9

SUBTRACTION – NUMBER LINE

① Write the answer to these addition facts using the number line.

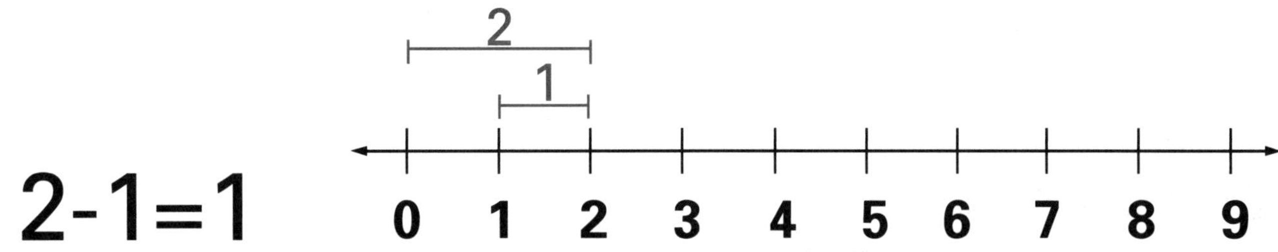

2-1=1

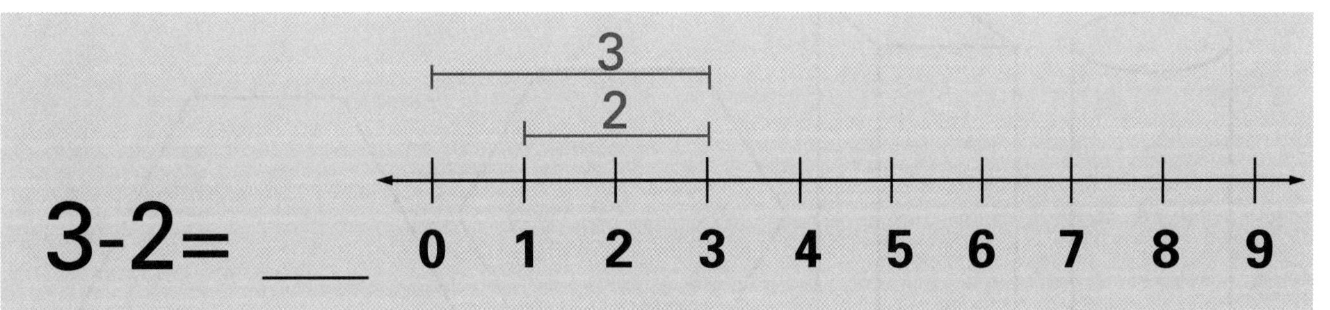

3-2= ___

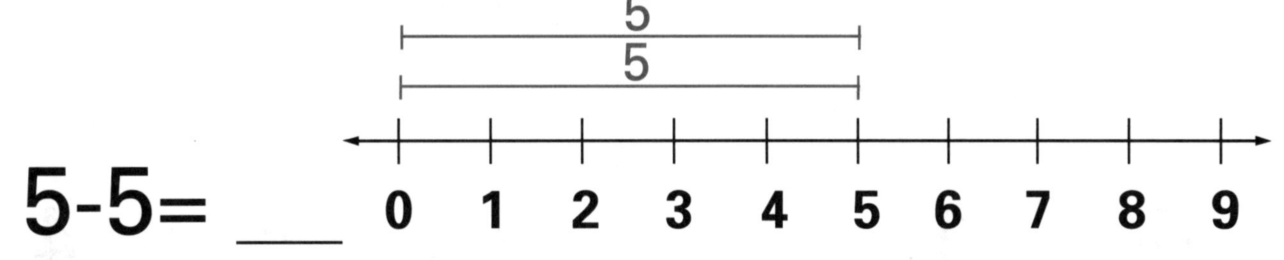

5-5= ___

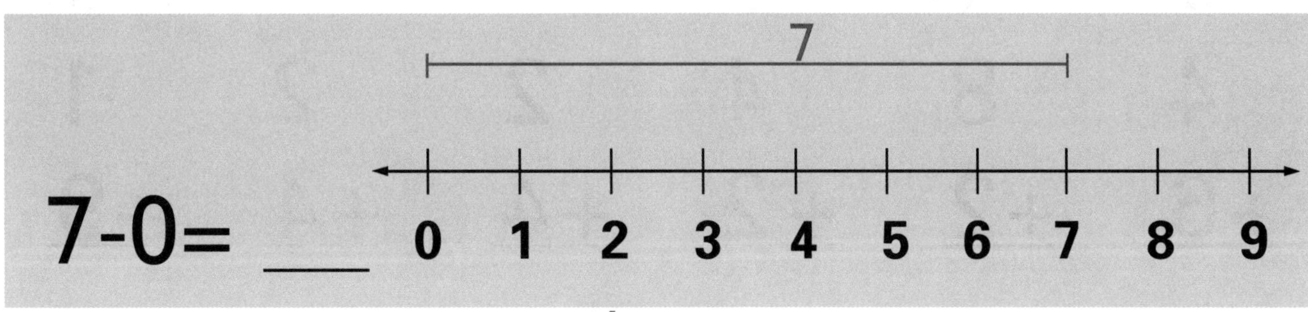

7-0= ___

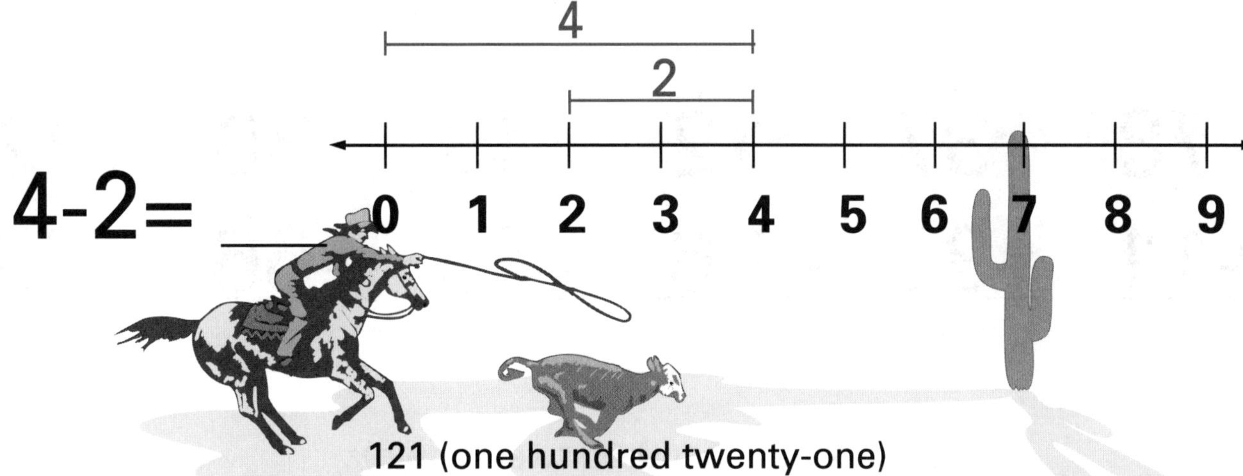

4-2= ___

② Write the correct time.

:

:

:

:

③ If divided into 2 parts, color $\frac{1}{2}$.

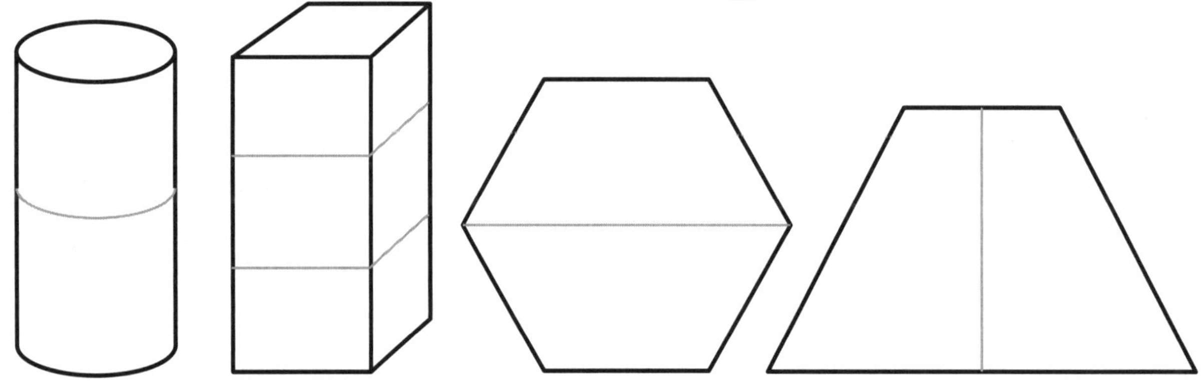

④ Write the answers.

$$\begin{array}{r} 5 \\ 4 \\ +6 \\ \hline \end{array} \quad \begin{array}{r} 1 \\ 8 \\ +2 \\ \hline \end{array} \quad \begin{array}{r} 5 \\ 4 \\ +2 \\ \hline \end{array} \quad \begin{array}{r} 7 \\ 2 \\ +4 \\ \hline \end{array} \quad \begin{array}{r} 6 \\ 2 \\ +4 \\ \hline \end{array} \quad \begin{array}{r} 4 \\ 1 \\ +9 \\ \hline \end{array}$$

$$\begin{array}{r} 78 \\ +11 \\ \hline \end{array} \quad \begin{array}{r} 37 \\ +32 \\ \hline \end{array} \quad \begin{array}{r} 12 \\ +56 \\ \hline \end{array} \quad \begin{array}{r} 43 \\ +45 \\ \hline \end{array} \quad \begin{array}{r} 30 \\ +66 \\ \hline \end{array} \quad \begin{array}{r} 22 \\ +20 \\ \hline \end{array}$$

MONEY – PENNIES AND DIMES

① Write the number on the line.

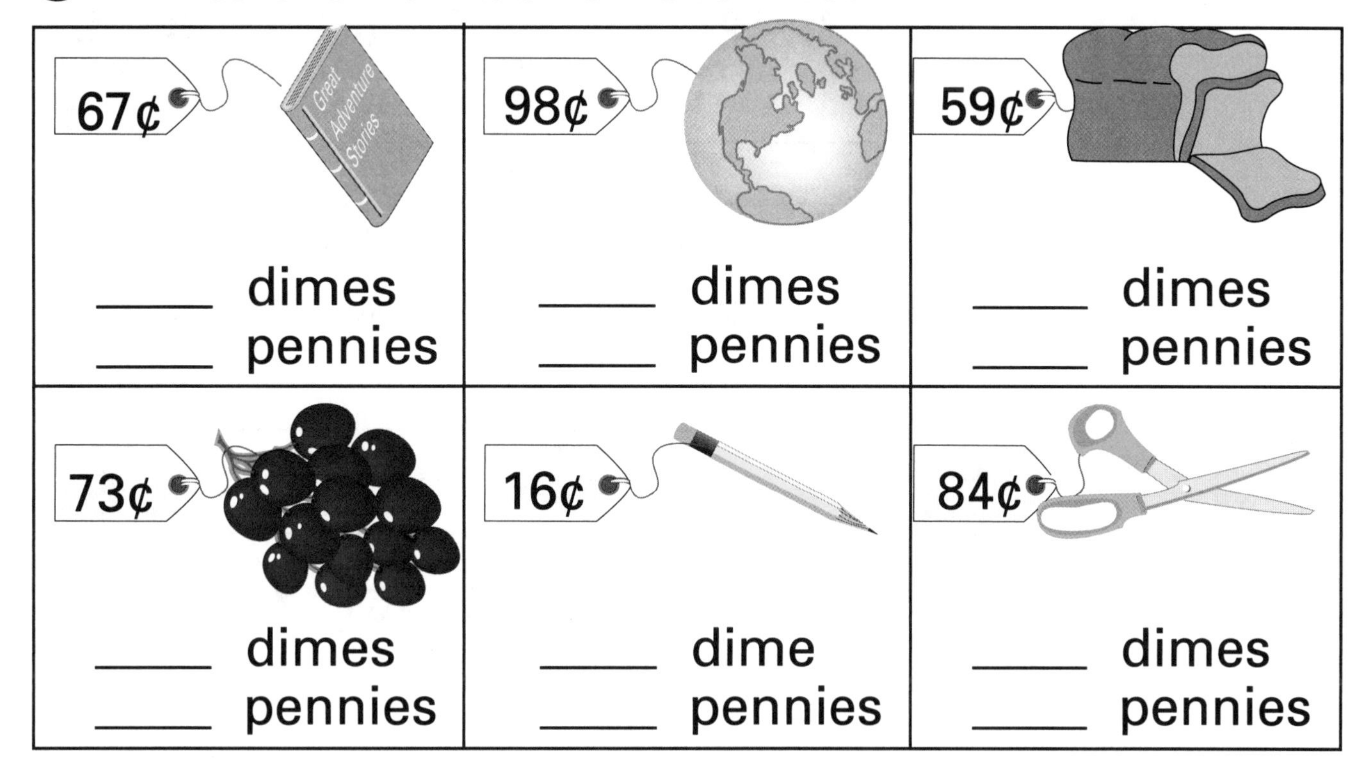

67¢	98¢	59¢
_____ dimes _____ pennies	_____ dimes _____ pennies	_____ dimes _____ pennies
73¢	**16¢**	**84¢**
_____ dimes _____ pennies	_____ dime _____ pennies	_____ dimes _____ pennies

② Write the correct time.

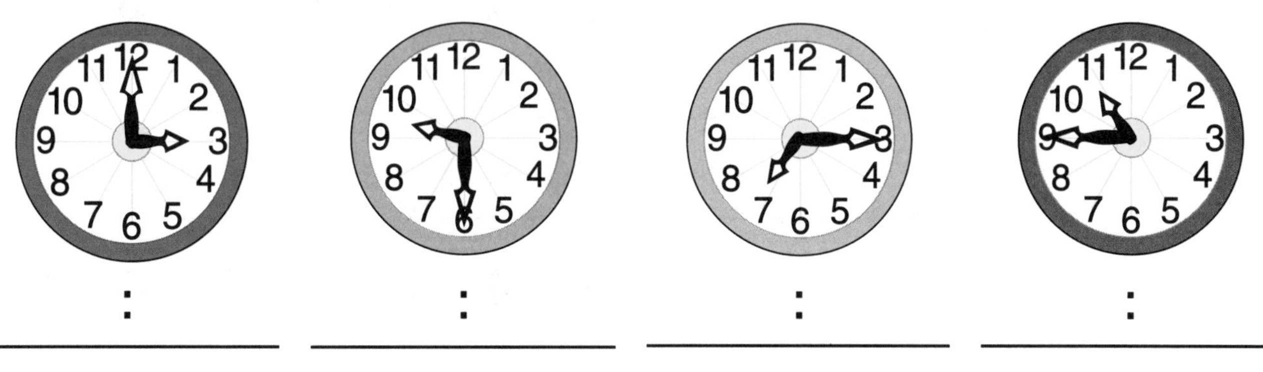

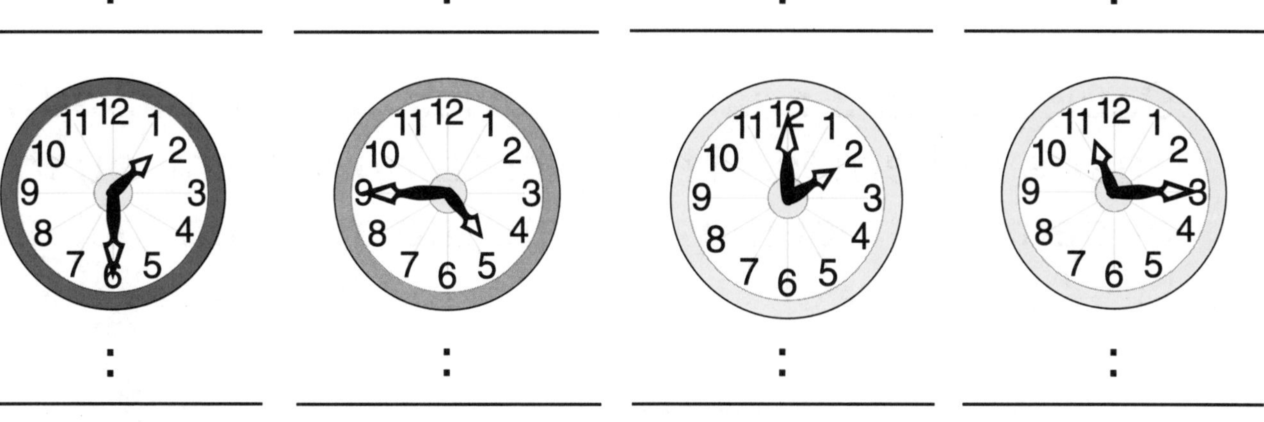

③ **Write the subtraction fact.**

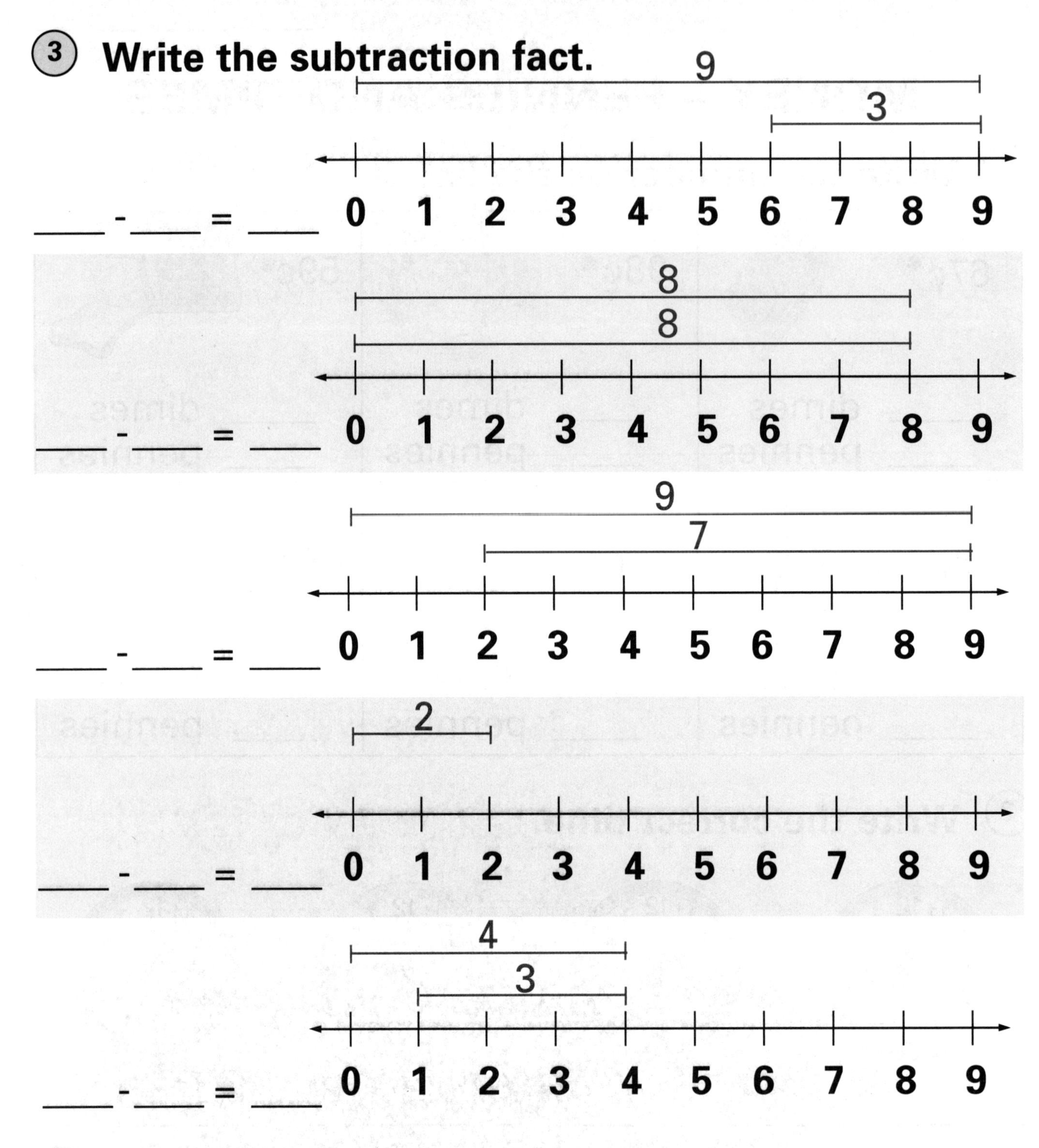

④ Doug picked 3 quarts of berries. Joyce picked 7 quarts of berries. They picked how many quarts of berries altogether? Write the addition fact and label the answer.

____ + ____ = ____ ______________

Lesson 57

INCHES

1 **Measure the lines with an inch ruler. Write the answers.**

_____ **inches**

_____ **inches**

_____ **inches**

2 **Draw dimes and pennies for each object.**

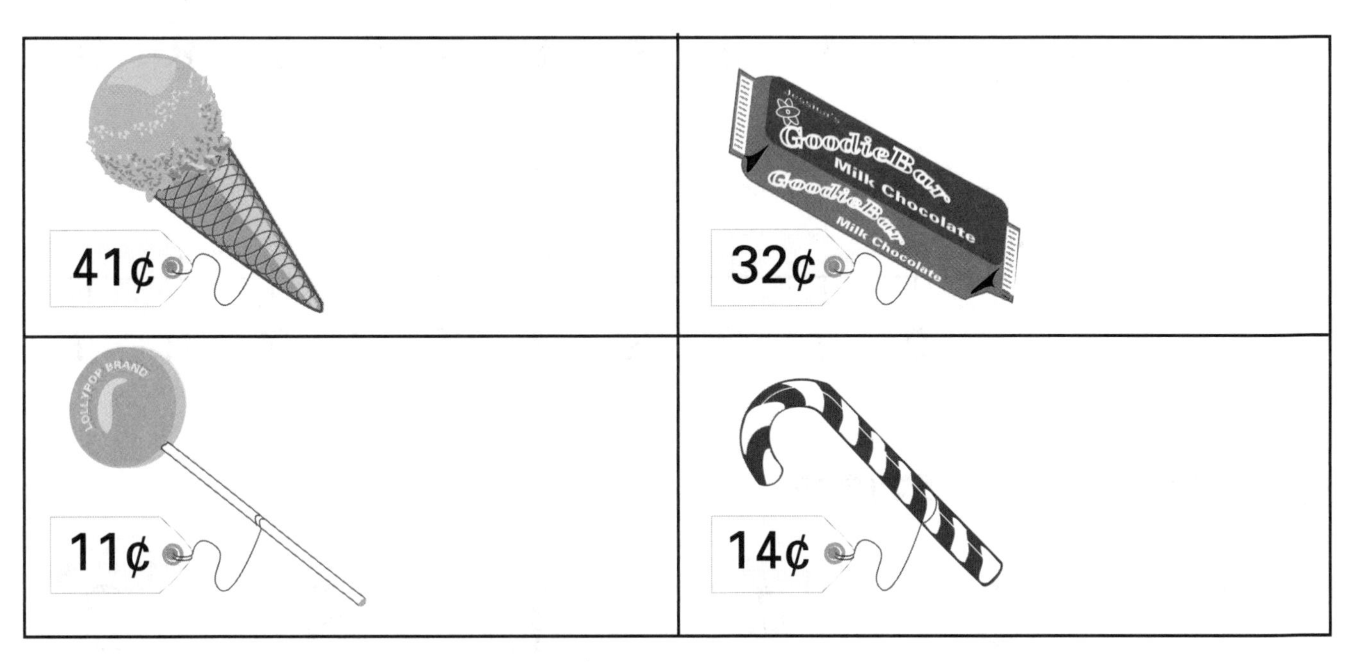

3 Alice has 6 pieces of candy. Karen gave Alice 8 more pieces of candy. How many pieces of candy does Alice have altogether? Label the answer.

_____ + _____ = _____ ______________

④ Write the subtraction fact.

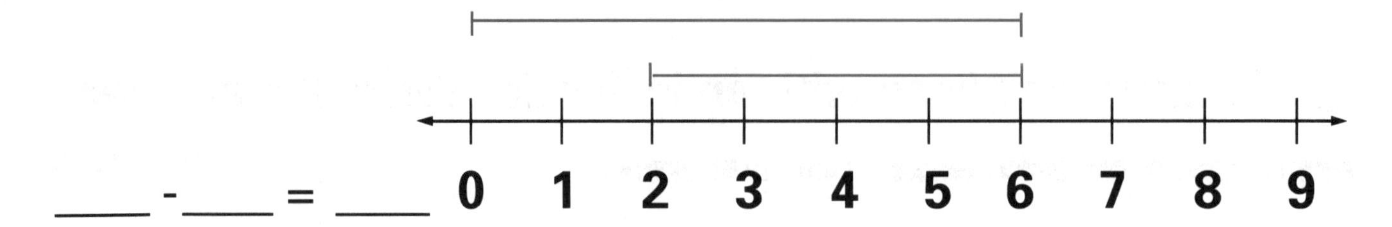

____ - ____ = ____

____ - ____ = ____

____ - ____ = ____ 0 1 2 3 4 5 6 7 8 9

____ - ____ = ____ 0 1 2 3 4 5 6 7 8 9

⑤ Write the answers.

7	5	4	1	9	2
2	4	3	6	0	7
+6	+8	+9	+9	+5	+6

NUMBER ORDER – ORDINAL NUMBERS

① **Write first, second, third, fourth, or fifth in the blanks.**

The ship is the ____________ toy.
The teddy bear is the ____________ toy.
The airplane is the ____________ toy.
The doll is the ____________ toy.
The car is the ____________ toy.

② **Circle the number of dimes and pennies needed.**

34¢ 23¢ 51¢ 75¢ 62¢

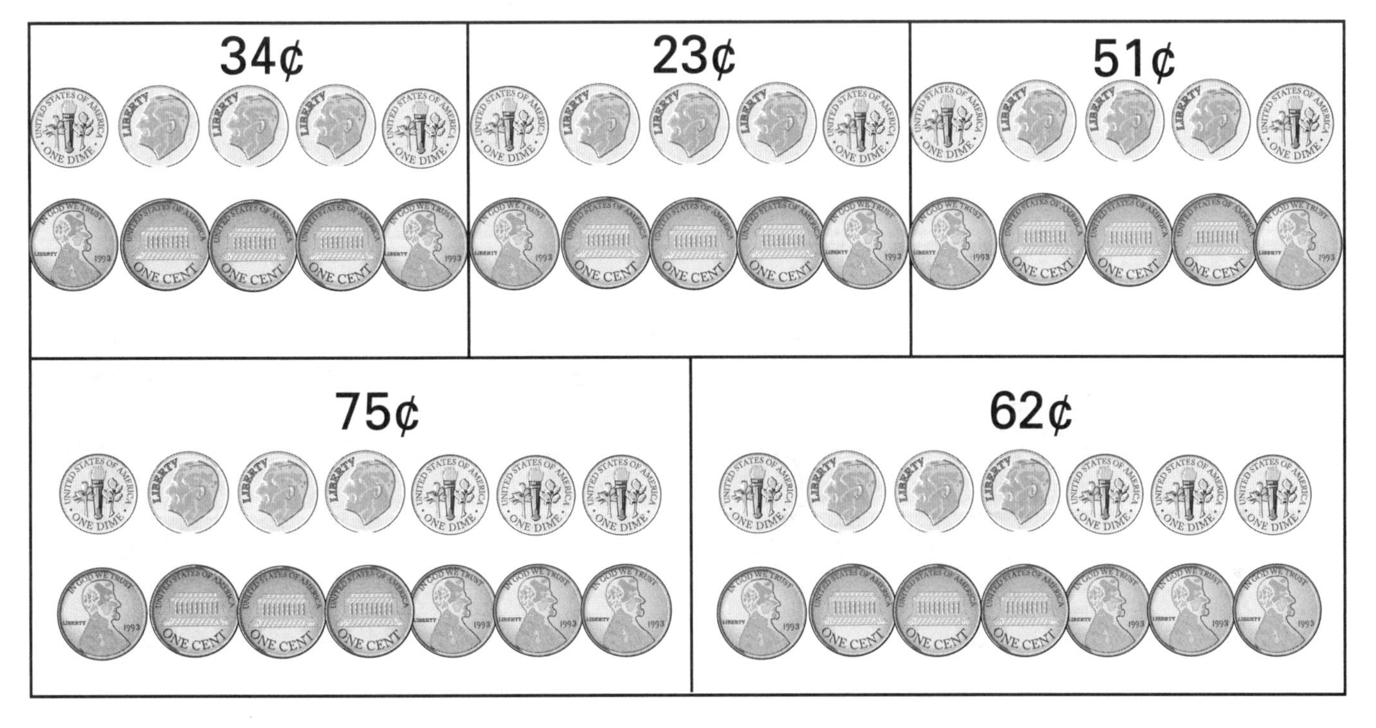

③ Draw the subtraction fact on the number line.

7-2=5

0 1 2 3 4 5 6 7 8 9

5-3=2

0 1 2 3 4 5 6 7 8 9

9-4=5

0 1 2 3 4 5 6 7 8 9

8-6=2

0 1 2 3 4 5 6 7 8 9

6-3=3

0 1 2 3 4 5 6 7 8 9

④ Write the answers.

$$\begin{array}{r} 7 \\ 2 \\ +5 \\ \hline \end{array} \quad \begin{array}{r} 3 \\ 6 \\ +4 \\ \hline \end{array} \quad \begin{array}{r} 7 \\ +5 \\ \hline \end{array} \quad \begin{array}{r} 8 \\ +7 \\ \hline \end{array} \quad \begin{array}{r} 3 \\ 3 \\ +3 \\ \hline \end{array} \quad \begin{array}{r} 3 \\ 4 \\ +2 \\ \hline \end{array}$$

PLACE VALUE

① **Write the numbers.**

5 tens = ____ 8 tens = ____ 9 tens = ____

7 tens = ____ 3 tens = ____ 4 tens = ____

1 ten = ____ 2 tens = ____ 6 tens = ____

② **Write the value of each set.**

____¢

____¢

____¢

____¢

③ **Counting by 10's, write the number that comes before and after.**

____ 10 ____ ____ 50 ____ ____ 40 ____

____ 70 ____ ____ 30 ____ ____ 90 ____

④ **Write the answers using the number line.**

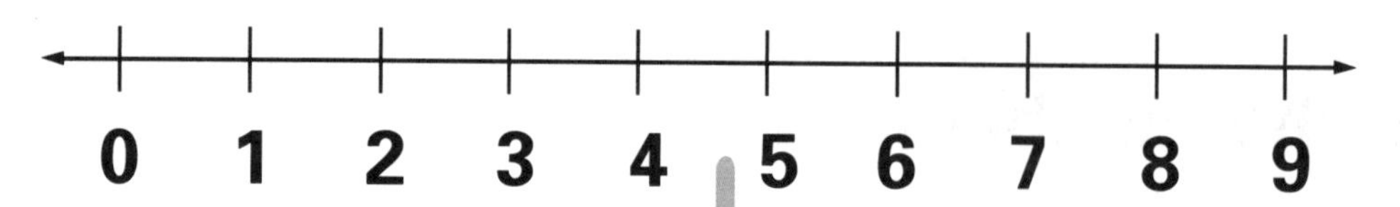

2 - 2 = ___

6 - 2 = ___

7 - 3 = ___

9 - 1 = ___

4 - 1 = ___

5 - 4 = ___

8 - 4 = ___

9 - 4 = ___

5 - 0 = ___

6 - 6 = ___

⑤ Alice made her brother Joe's bed for 8 mornings. Then she made Jack's bed for 7 mornings. How many mornings did she make a bed for her brothers? Label the answer.

___ ___ ___ ___________

Allen had 9 crayons in his desk. He found 7 more in his book bag. How many crayons did he have altogether? Label the answer.

___ ___ ___ ___________

TEST 6

① Write the correct time. 4 pts. total for this exercise.

② Shade $\frac{1}{2}$ of each object. 3 pts. total for this exercise.

③ Shade $\frac{1}{4}$ of each object. 3 pts. total for this exercise.

4 **Counting by 10's, write the number that comes before and after.** 18 pts. total for this exercise.

___ 60 ___	___ 90 ___	___ 40 ___
___ 50 ___	___ 20 ___	___ 80 ___
___ 10 ___	___ 70 ___	___ 30 ___

5 **Write the answers.** 12 pts. total for this exercise.

$$\begin{array}{r} 7 \\ 1 \\ +3 \\ \hline \end{array} \quad \begin{array}{r} 5 \\ 3 \\ +4 \\ \hline \end{array} \quad \begin{array}{r} 4 \\ 3 \\ +2 \\ \hline \end{array} \quad \begin{array}{r} 7 \\ 1 \\ +1 \\ \hline \end{array} \quad \begin{array}{r} 5 \\ 4 \\ +7 \\ \hline \end{array} \quad \begin{array}{r} 2 \\ 6 \\ +1 \\ \hline \end{array}$$

$$\begin{array}{r} 63 \\ +13 \\ \hline \end{array} \quad \begin{array}{r} 42 \\ +21 \\ \hline \end{array} \quad \begin{array}{r} 83 \\ +16 \\ \hline \end{array} \quad \begin{array}{r} 75 \\ +24 \\ \hline \end{array} \quad \begin{array}{r} 23 \\ +\ 6 \\ \hline \end{array} \quad \begin{array}{r} 35 \\ +11 \\ \hline \end{array}$$

6 Mae had 5 pennies in her bank. Her mother gave her 8 more to put in her bank. Mae's bank now has how many pennies in it altogether? Label the answer. 4 pts.

___ ___ ___ __________

44 pts. Total

WORD NUMBERS – ELEVEN TO ONE HUNDRED

① **Write the number in the blank.**

eighteen ____

forty ____

eleven ____

ninety ____

sixteen ____

twenty ____

fifteen ____

seventy ____

eighty ____

twelve ____

② **Write the numbers in the blanks.**

34 = ____ tens+ ____ ones

12 = ____ ten + ____ ones

27 = ____ tens+ ____ ones

75 = ____ tens+ ____ ones

9 = ____ tens+ ____ ones

98 = ____ tens+ ____ ones

56 = ____ tens+ ____ ones

41 = ____ tens+ ____ one

83 = ____ tens+ ____ ones

60 = ____ tens+ ____ ones

③ **Draw the number of nickels needed.**

45¢

15¢

30¢

④ **Write the answers using the number line.**

0 1 2 3 4 5 6 7 8 9

3 - 0 = ___	4 - 4 = ___	5 - 3 = ___
7 - 2 = ___	1 - 1 = ___	6 - 1 = ___
8 - 3 = ___	6 - 5 = ___	7 - 6 = ___

⑤ **Write the answers.**

5	3	6	5	4	6
3	4	2	4	4	1
+6	+7	+9	+9	+8	+7

5	6	6	5	6	5
+9	+7	+8	+8	+9	+7

54	72	14	16
+45	+17	+13	+22

Lesson 61

SUBTRACTION – VERTICAL

① **Write the answers using the number line.**

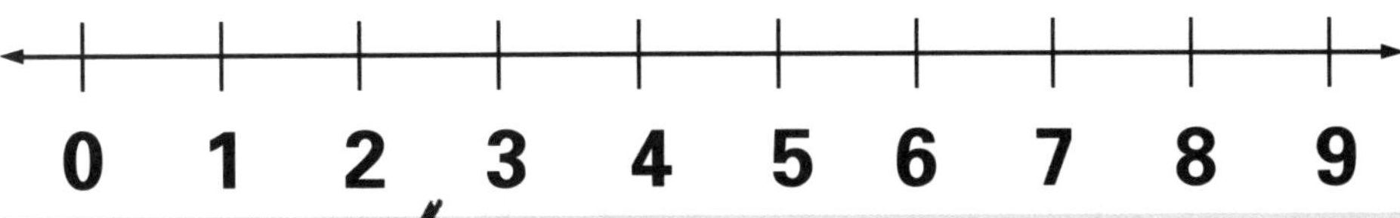

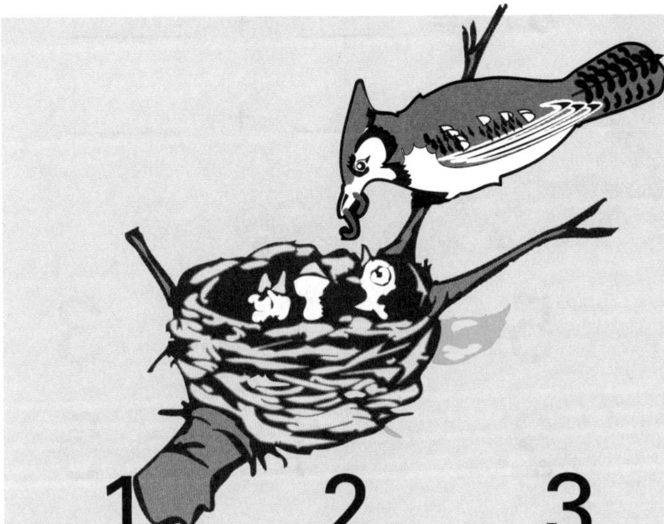

9-5= ☐

$$\begin{array}{r} 9 \\ -5 \\ \hline \end{array}$$

$$\begin{array}{r} 1 \\ -0 \\ \hline \end{array} \quad \begin{array}{r} 2 \\ -1 \\ \hline \end{array} \quad \begin{array}{r} 3 \\ -2 \\ \hline \end{array} \quad \begin{array}{r} 5 \\ -1 \\ \hline \end{array} \quad \begin{array}{r} 7 \\ -0 \\ \hline \end{array} \quad \begin{array}{r} 6 \\ -3 \\ \hline \end{array}$$

$$\begin{array}{r} 5 \\ -5 \\ \hline \end{array} \quad \begin{array}{r} 7 \\ -4 \\ \hline \end{array} \quad \begin{array}{r} 4 \\ -0 \\ \hline \end{array} \quad \begin{array}{r} 8 \\ -1 \\ \hline \end{array} \quad \begin{array}{r} 8 \\ -5 \\ \hline \end{array} \quad \begin{array}{r} 4 \\ -2 \\ \hline \end{array}$$

② Anna picked 6 lemons from the tree. Eva picked 8 more. How many lemons did the girls pick altogether? Label the answer.

____ + ____ = ____ ________________

③ **Write the value of the tens and ones.**

72 = _____ + _____

57 = _____ + _____

38 = _____ + _____

84 = _____ + _____

16 = _____ + _____

43 = _____ + _____

61 = _____ + _____

25 = _____ + _____

④ **Write the answers.**

$$\begin{array}{r}6\\2\\+3\\\hline\end{array}\quad\begin{array}{r}1\\2\\+7\\\hline\end{array}\quad\begin{array}{r}2\\3\\+8\\\hline\end{array}\quad\begin{array}{r}5\\2\\+9\\\hline\end{array}\quad\begin{array}{r}7\\1\\+2\\\hline\end{array}\quad\begin{array}{r}3\\5\\+9\\\hline\end{array}$$

$$\begin{array}{r}6\\2\\+4\\\hline\end{array}\quad\begin{array}{r}4\\3\\+5\\\hline\end{array}\quad\begin{array}{r}6\\3\\+2\\\hline\end{array}\quad\begin{array}{r}6\\2\\+6\\\hline\end{array}\quad\begin{array}{r}7\\1\\+5\\\hline\end{array}\quad\begin{array}{r}3\\5\\+7\\\hline\end{array}$$

$$\begin{array}{r}42\\+36\\\hline\end{array}\quad\begin{array}{r}82\\+\ 6\\\hline\end{array}$$

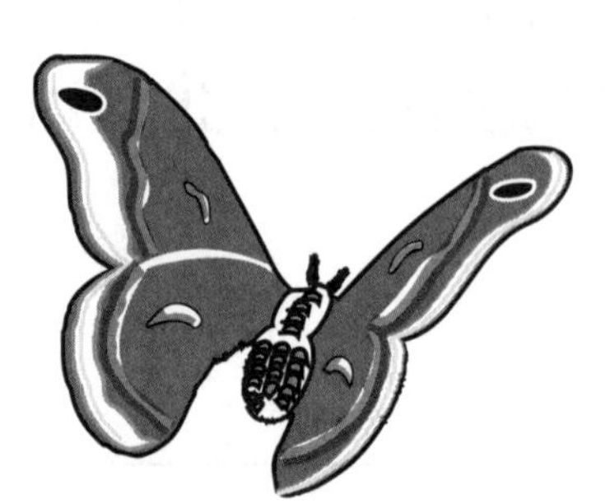

$$\begin{array}{r}41\\+58\\\hline\end{array}\quad\begin{array}{r}45\\+24\\\hline\end{array}$$

WORD NUMBERS – TWENTY TO ONE HUNDRED

① Match the word number to the number.

twenty-one	34
sixty-eight	21
thirty-four	89
eighty-nine	68
forty-two	96
ninety-six	57
fifty-seven	42

forty-six	95
ninety-five	71
fifty-three	46
seventy-one	53
twenty-two	37
sixty-four	22
thirty-seven	64

② Write the problems vertically. Write the answers.

$16 + 23 =$

$17 + 2 =$

$43 + 36 =$

$10 + 11 =$

③ **Write the answers.**

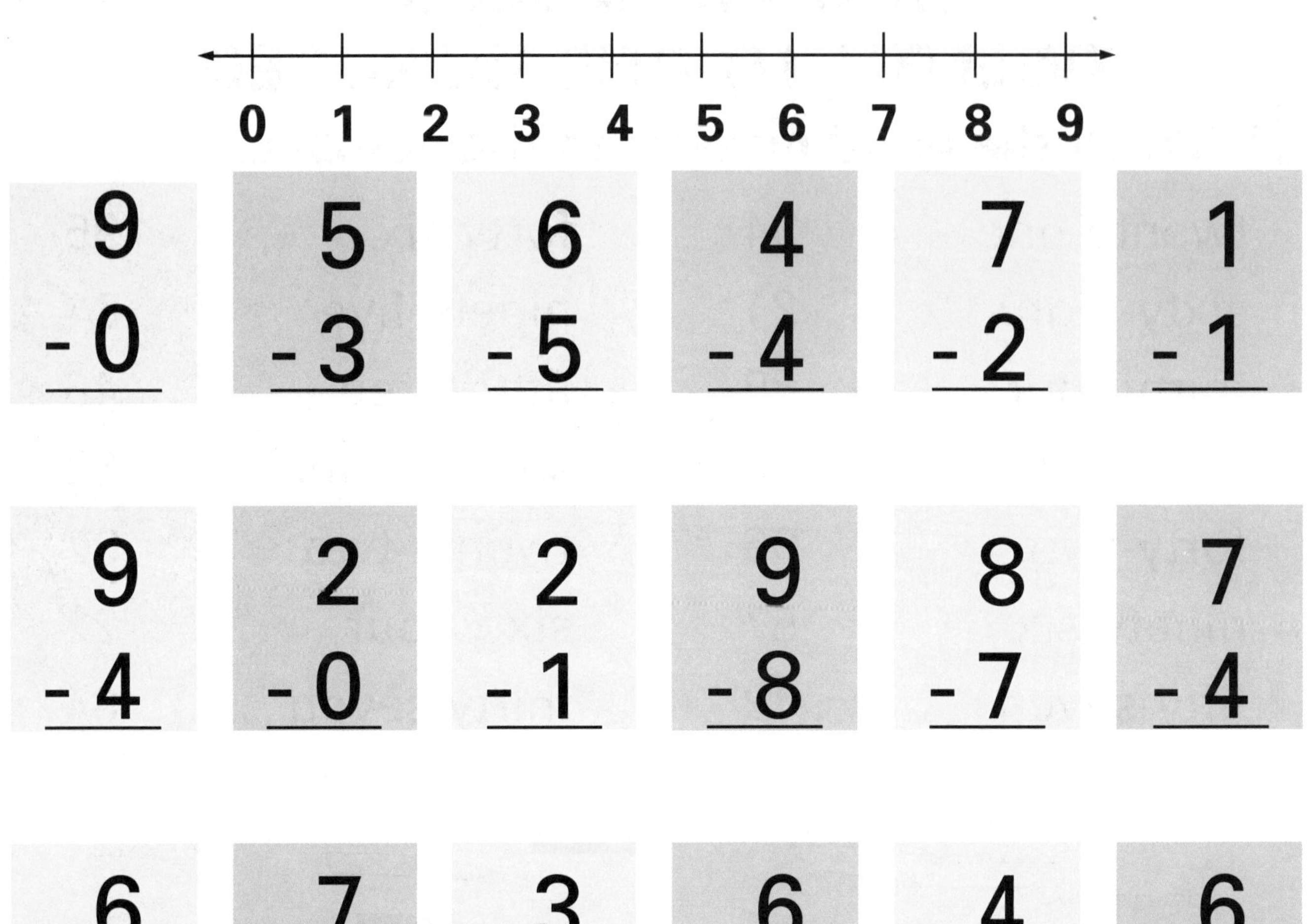

④ Roy had 5 paper airplanes. Rod gave him 7 more. Roy now has how many paper airplanes altogether? Label the answer.

____ + ____ = ____ ________________

Lori skipped rope 9 times. Jan skipped rope only 4 times. How many times did they skip rope altogether? Label the answer.

____ + ____ = ____ ________________

SHOW YOUR SKILLS

① **Write the answers.**

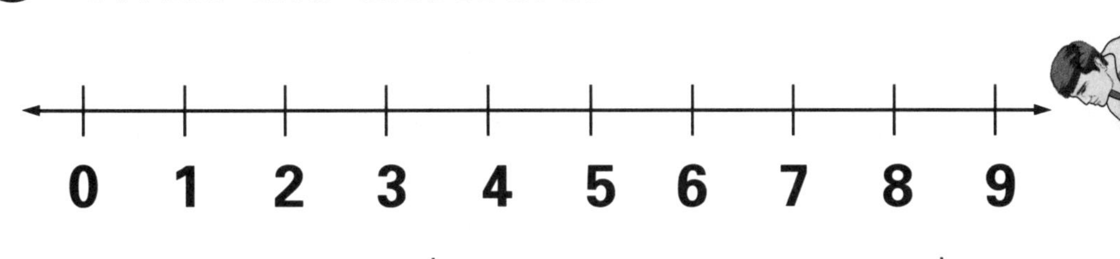

$9-6=$	$8-3=$	$1-0=$
$4-1=$	$5-0=$	$8-2=$

$\begin{array}{r}8\\-8\\\hline\end{array}$	$\begin{array}{r}2\\-0\\\hline\end{array}$	$\begin{array}{r}4\\-3\\\hline\end{array}$	$\begin{array}{r}5\\-2\\\hline\end{array}$	$\begin{array}{r}9\\-9\\\hline\end{array}$	$\begin{array}{r}6\\-4\\\hline\end{array}$
$\begin{array}{r}7\\-1\\\hline\end{array}$	$\begin{array}{r}7\\-5\\\hline\end{array}$	$\begin{array}{r}8\\-0\\\hline\end{array}$	$\begin{array}{r}8\\-4\\\hline\end{array}$	$\begin{array}{r}3\\-3\\\hline\end{array}$	$\begin{array}{r}6\\-0\\\hline\end{array}$

② Write the number.

forty-one	____	twenty-nine	____
ninety-two	____	fifty-one	____
sixty-five	____	thirty-eight	____
thirty-six	____	ninety-three	____
eighty-four	____	seventy-two	____

③ Draw the number of quarters needed.

75¢ ____________________

50¢ ____________________

④ Write the answers.

1	5	3	7	3	2
2	3	4	2	6	5
+7	+6	+7	+8	+3	+9

40	19	24	55	54	63
+47	+20	+43	+20	+22	+14

FRACTIONS – ONE FOURTH

① **Divide each object into fourths. Shade $\frac{1}{4}$.**

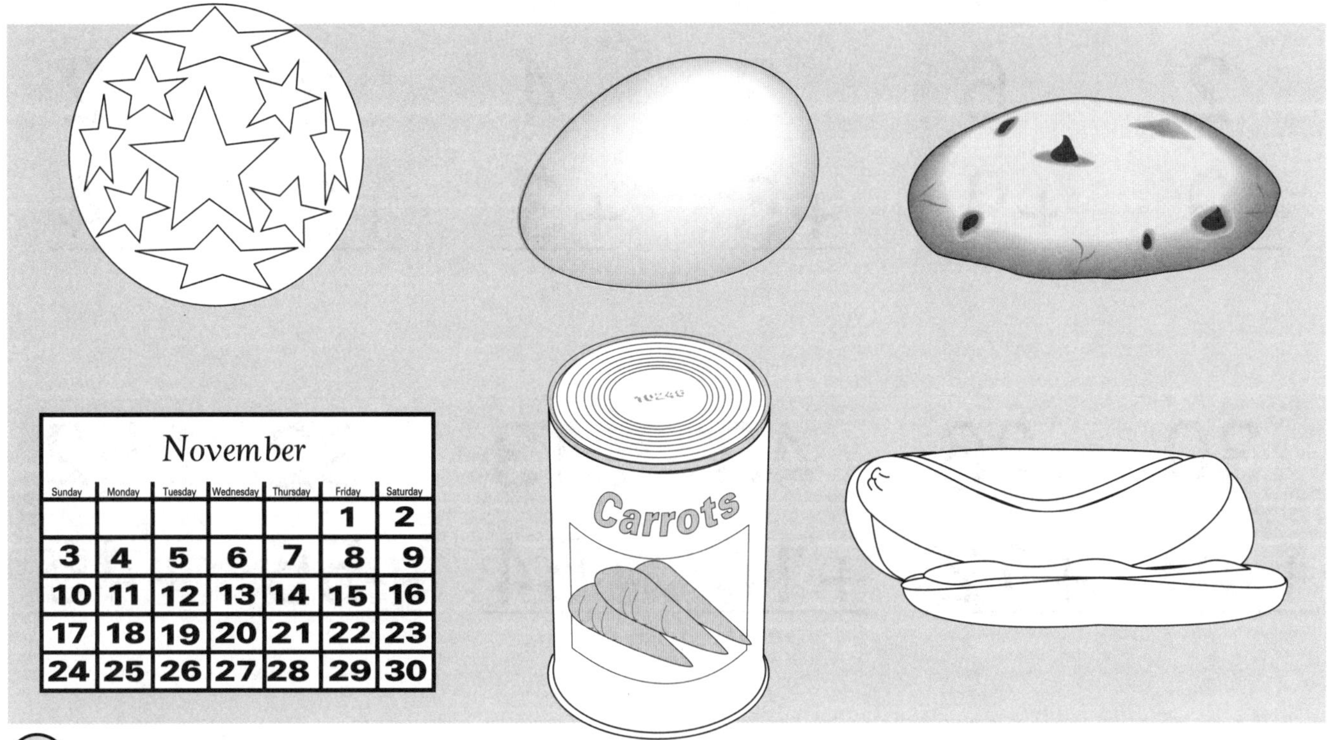

② **Write the value of each coin.**

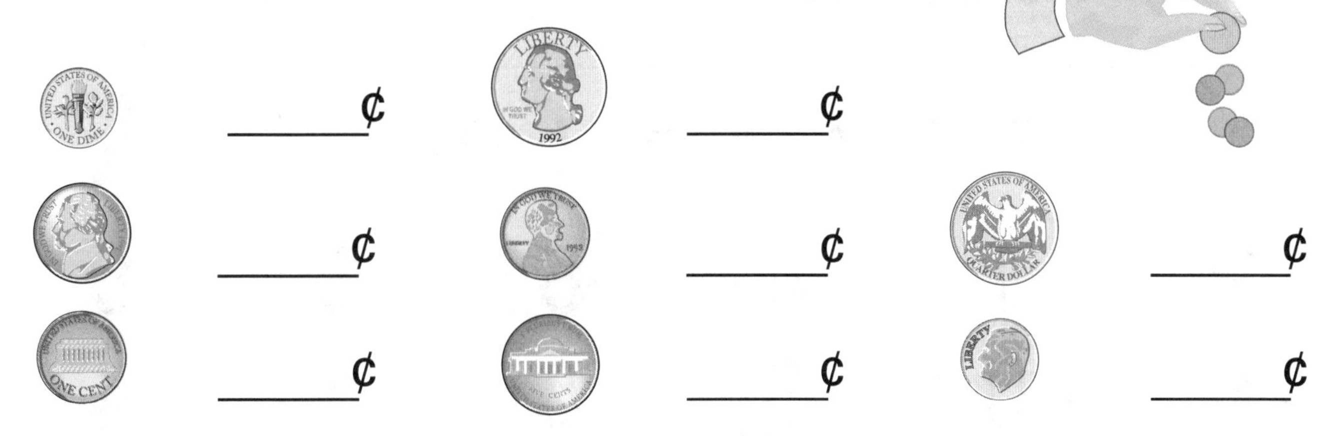

③ Polly dusted 6 rows of library books. Sally dusted the next 8 rows. How many rows did they dust altogether?

④ Write the answers.

7	3	2	3	7	6
2	6	2	4	2	2
+9	+9	+5	+3	+8	+4

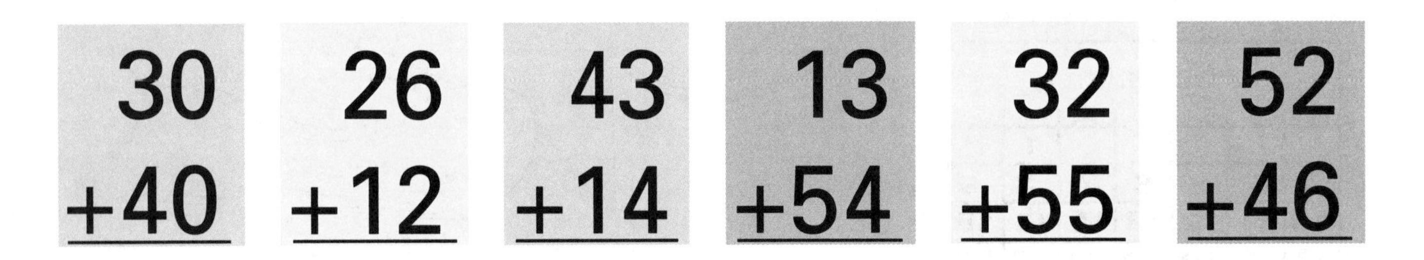

⑤ Write the answers.

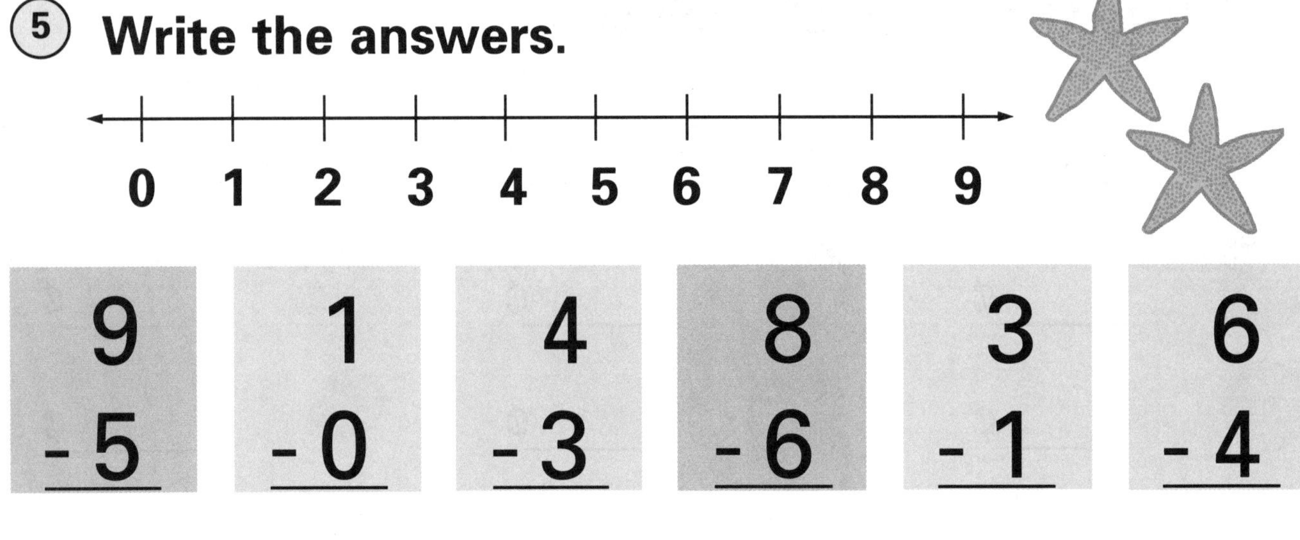

EVEN NUMBERS

① **Color all the even numbers.**

1	2	3	4	5	6	7	8	9	10	11	12
13	14	15	16	17	18	19	20	21	22	23	24
25	26	27	28	29	30	31	32	33	34	35	36
37	38	39	40	41	42	43	44	45	46	47	48

② **Circle the shapes that have $\frac{1}{4}$ colored.**

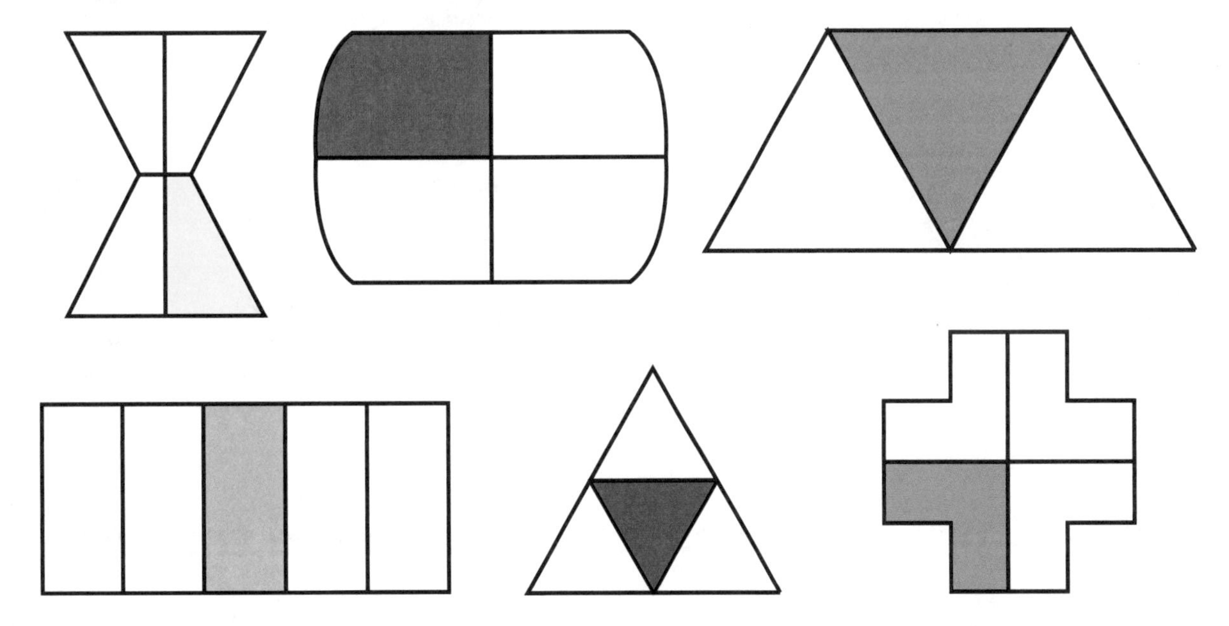

③ Ed colored 5 pictures in the coloring book. Rex colored 7 pictures. How many pictures in the book did they color altogether?

4 **Write the answers.**

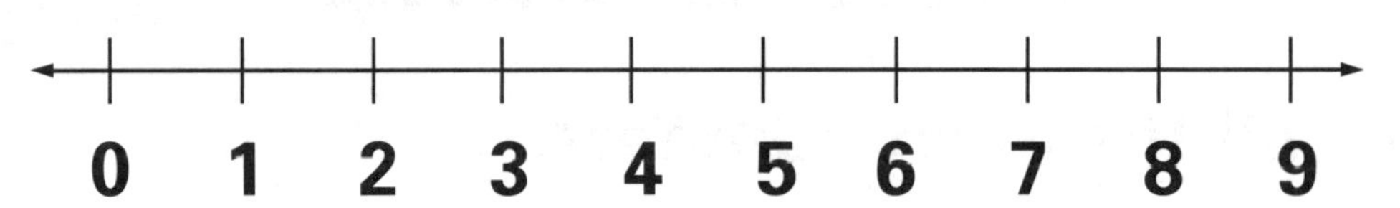

$\begin{array}{r} 2 \\ -1 \\ \hline \end{array}$	$\begin{array}{r} 9 \\ -9 \\ \hline \end{array}$	$\begin{array}{r} 7 \\ -6 \\ \hline \end{array}$	$\begin{array}{r} 6 \\ -1 \\ \hline \end{array}$	$\begin{array}{r} 4 \\ -1 \\ \hline \end{array}$	$\begin{array}{r} 8 \\ -0 \\ \hline \end{array}$
$\begin{array}{r} 7 \\ -1 \\ \hline \end{array}$	$\begin{array}{r} 9 \\ -5 \\ \hline \end{array}$	$\begin{array}{r} 8 \\ -6 \\ \hline \end{array}$	$\begin{array}{r} 7 \\ -5 \\ \hline \end{array}$	$\begin{array}{r} 5 \\ -1 \\ \hline \end{array}$	$\begin{array}{r} 7 \\ -3 \\ \hline \end{array}$
$\begin{array}{r} 9 \\ -8 \\ \hline \end{array}$	$\begin{array}{r} 9 \\ -6 \\ \hline \end{array}$	$\begin{array}{r} 7 \\ -0 \\ \hline \end{array}$	$\begin{array}{r} 5 \\ -4 \\ \hline \end{array}$	$\begin{array}{r} 8 \\ -7 \\ \hline \end{array}$	$\begin{array}{r} 7 \\ -7 \\ \hline \end{array}$

5 **Write < or > between each set. Read the set.**

3+4 ___ 10	7+5 ___ 16	6+3 ___ 11
9+4 ___ 15	7+7 ___ 7	2+6 ___ 7
4+5 ___ 8	6+5 ___ 14	7+2 ___ 11

FRACTIONS – ONE HALF AND ONE FOURTH

1 **Circle the picture that matches the fraction problem.**

Ann ate $\frac{1}{2}$ of a donut.

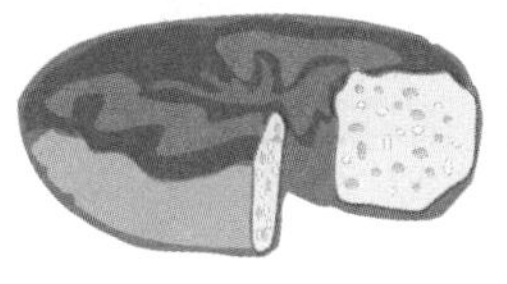
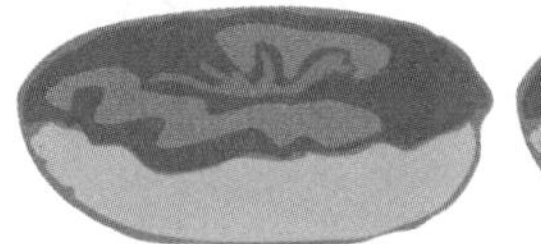
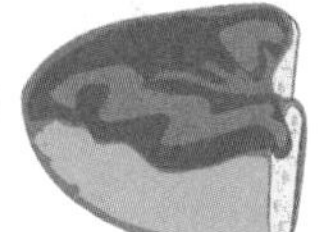

Karen ate $\frac{1}{4}$ of a pizza.

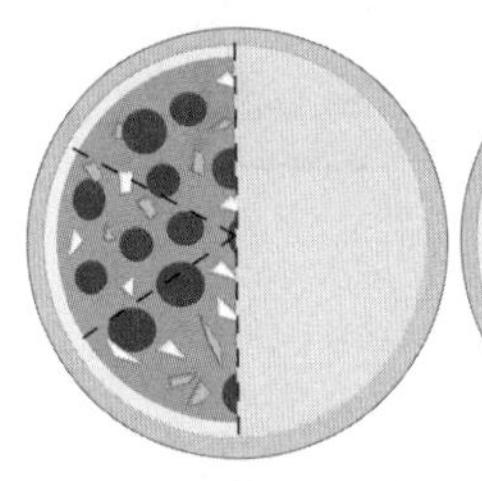
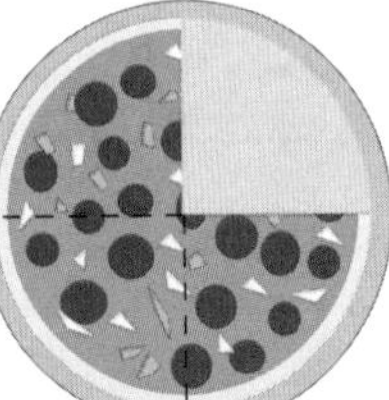
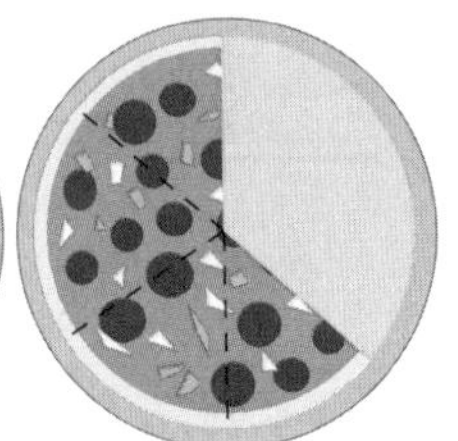

John ate $\frac{1}{2}$ of an apple pie.

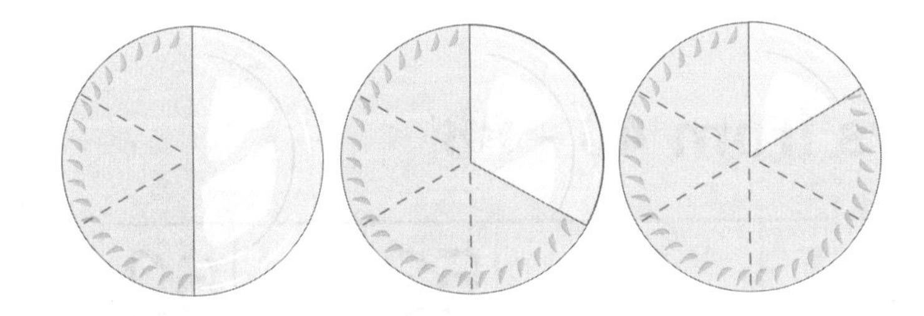

Susan ate $\frac{1}{4}$ of a watermelon slice.

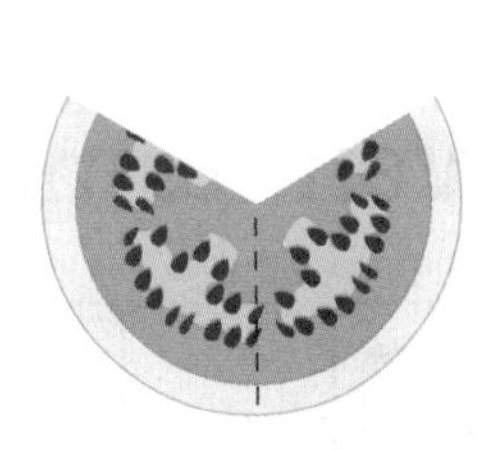
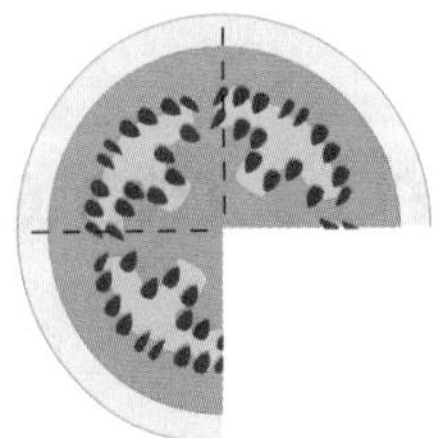
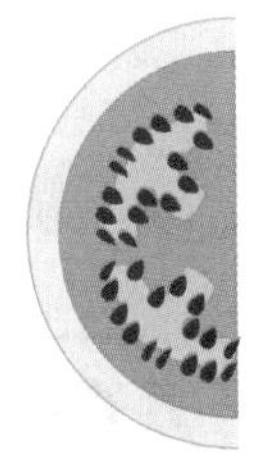

2 **Write the answers.**

4	3	3	5	7	5
2	5	6	2	2	3
+3	+2	+4	+9	+4	+6

③ Write the answers.

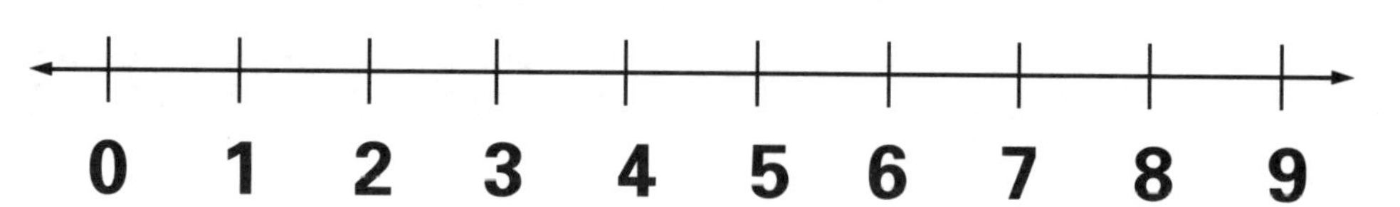

3 - 1	9 - 9	5 - 4	2 - 0	8 - 3	6 - 6
4 - 2	5 - 2	3 - 3	7 - 2	6 - 4	8 - 1

④ Write the even numbers from 40 - 86.

40			46						58		62
64						76					86

⑤ Write < or > between each set.

5 ____ ||||

7 ____ 卌 卌

3 ____ ||

6 ____ 卌

2 ____ |||

4 ____ 卌 ||

EQUAL AND NOT EQUAL

(1) **Write = or ≠ between each set.**

$\frac{1}{2}$ ____

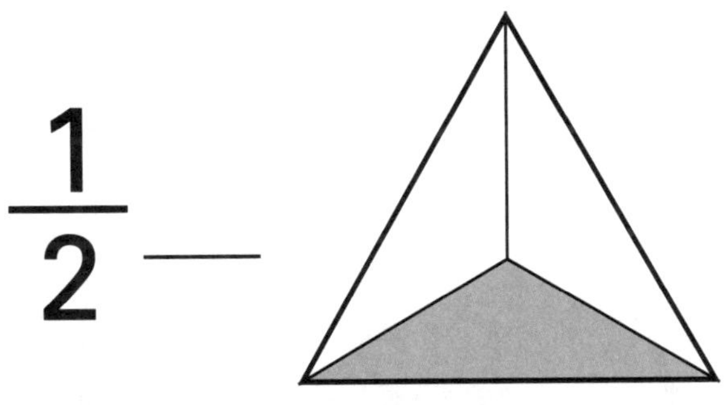
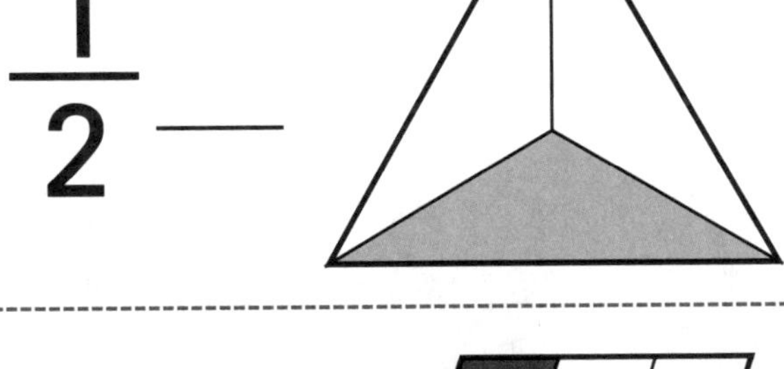

$\frac{1}{3}$ ____

$\frac{1}{4}$ ____

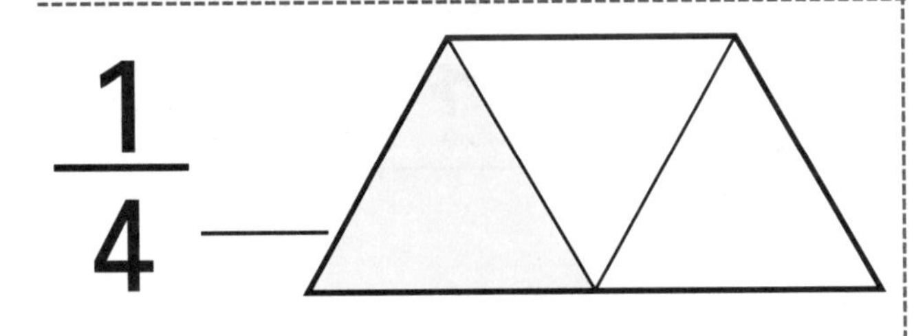

$\frac{1}{6}$ ____

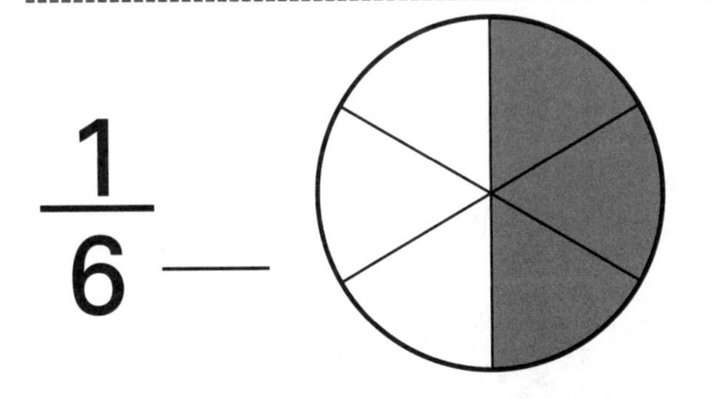

$\frac{1}{4}$ ____

$\frac{1}{4}$ ____

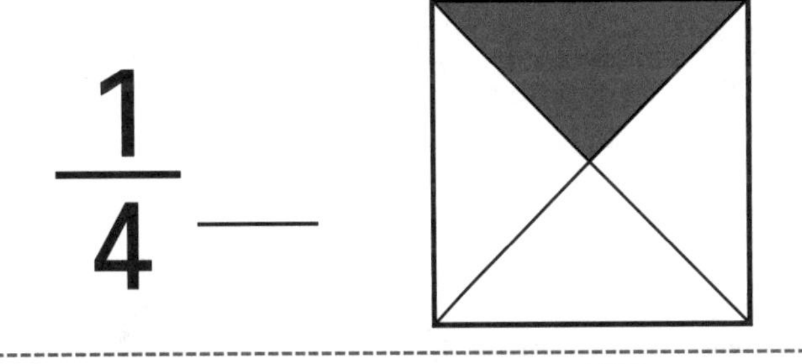

$\frac{1}{2}$ ____

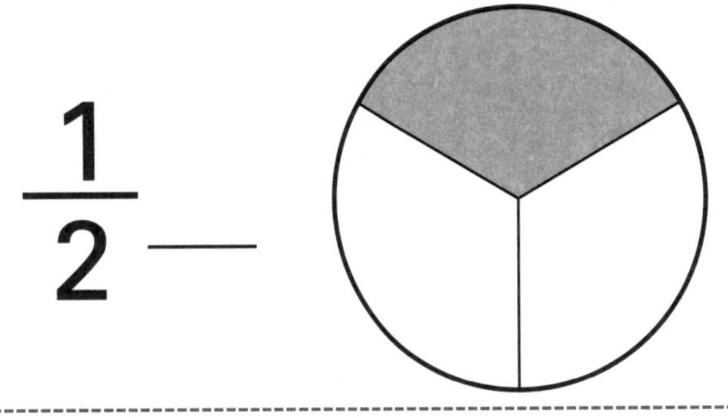

$\frac{1}{5}$ ____

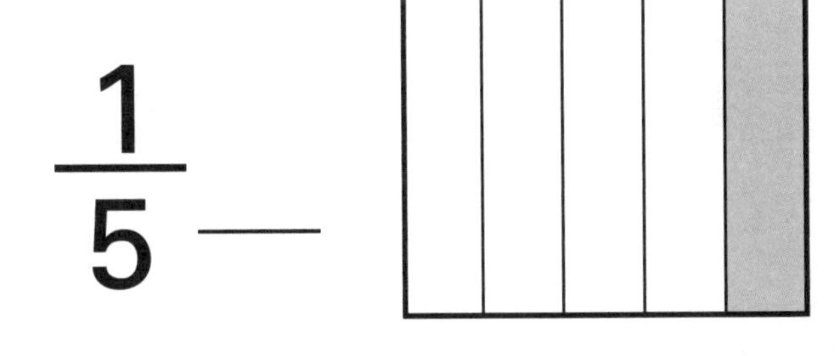

$\frac{1}{2}$ ____

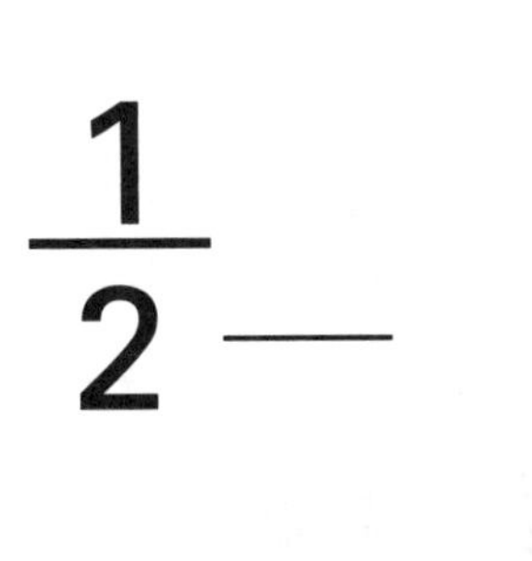

$\frac{1}{3}$ ____

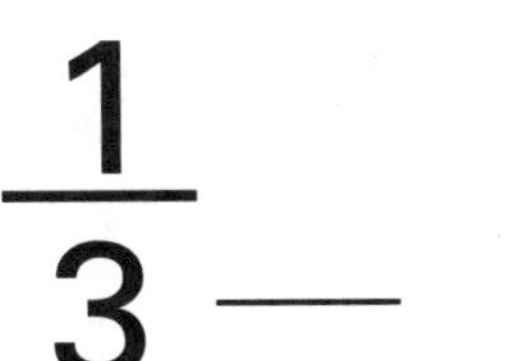
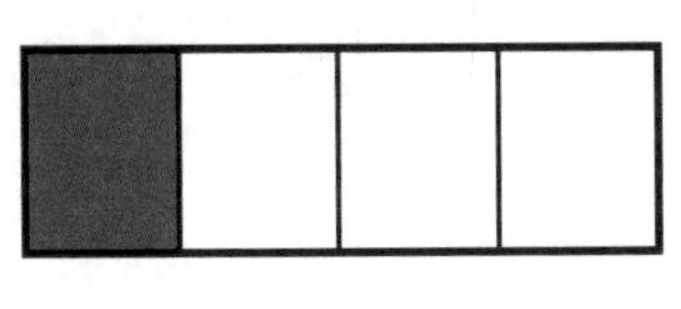

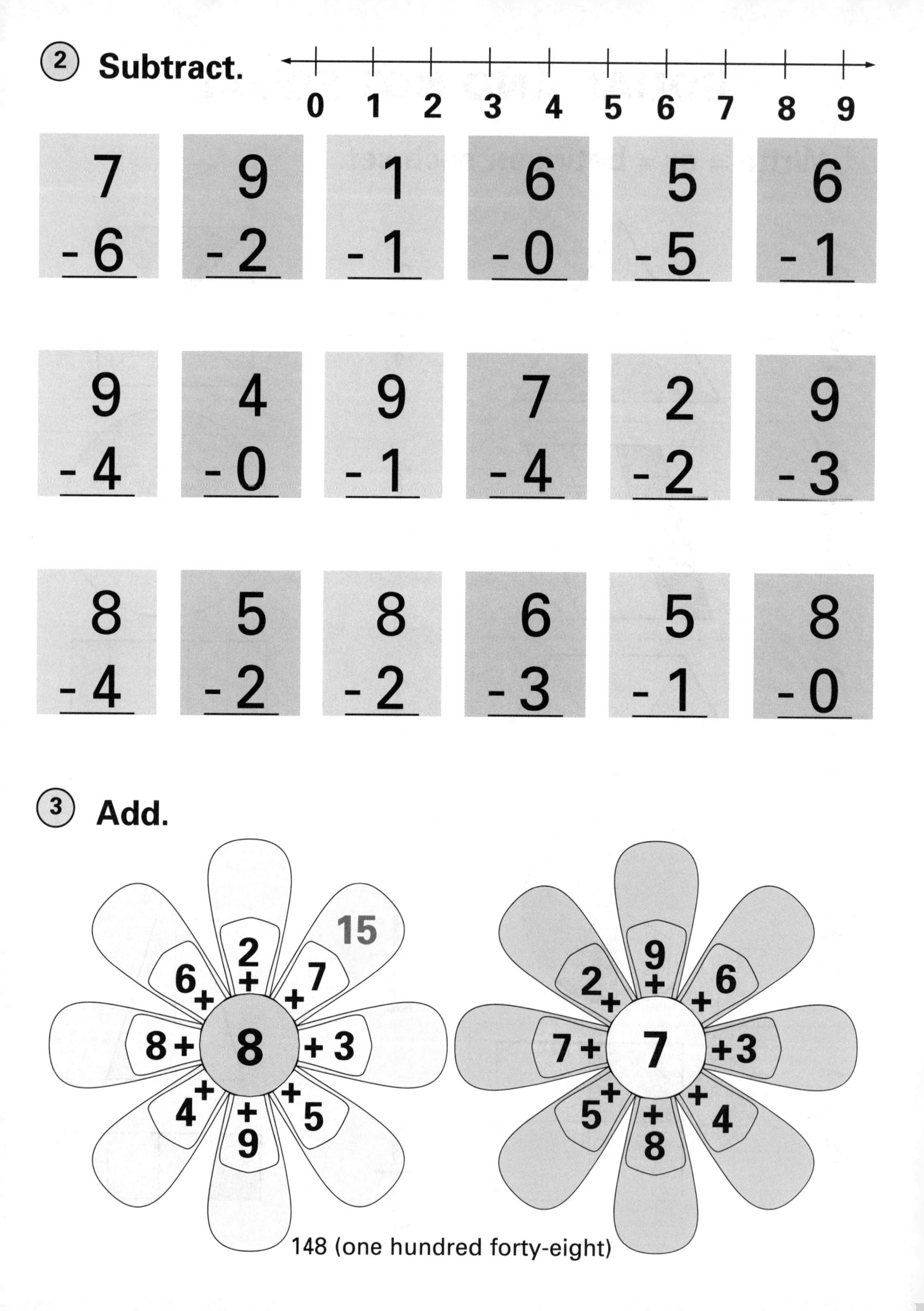
2 Subtract.
0 1 2 3 4 5 6 7 8 9
7 - 6
9 - 2
1 - 1
6 - 0
5 - 5
6 - 1
9 - 4
4 - 0
9 - 1
7 - 4
2 - 2
9 - 3
8 - 4
5 - 2
8 - 2
6 - 3
5 - 1
8 - 0
3 Add.
8
2 +
7 +
+ 3
+ 5
+ 9
4 +
8 +
6 +
15
7
9 +
6 +
+ 3
+ 4
+ 8
5 +
7 +
2 +

TIME – HOUR

① Draw the short hand for each clock.

3:00

10:00

7:00

1:00

② Write = or ≠ between each set.

fifteen	_____	50	thirty-six	_____	34
twenty-one	_____	21	twelve	_____	12
fourteen	_____	44	eighteen	_____	18
nine	_____	6	seventy-one	_____	71

③ There were 5 frogs on a lily pad. 4 more joined them. How many frogs were on the lily pad?

Freddy Frog ate 9 bugs. Fran Frog ate 4 bugs. How many bugs did the two frogs eat?

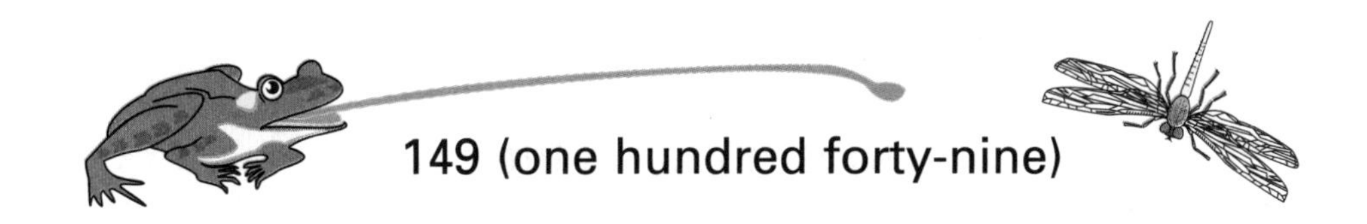

④ Write the problems vertically. Write the answers.

42 + 16 =	15+14 =
12+20 =	43+15 =

⑤ Subtract.

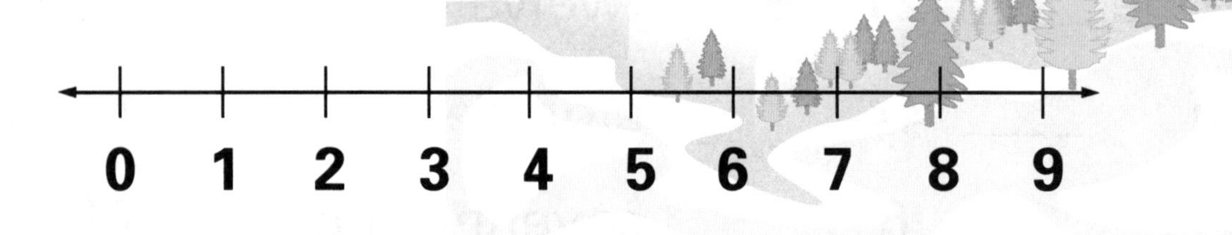

1 - 0	9 - 8	8 - 5	3 - 0	8 - 1	9 - 2
9 - 3	7 - 2	6 - 2	6 - 5	5 - 5	6 - 4

INCHES

① **Draw a line with the ruler.**

4 inches

•

3 inches

•

6 inches

•

5 inches

•

② **Draw both hands on the clock.**

③ There were 8 boys and 6 girls in a van going to the zoo. How many children were in the van?

④ **Add.**

23	56	15	17	83	17
+32	+13	+43	+62	+12	+42

7	1	6	3	7	6
2	6	2	4	2	2
+0	+9	+5	+3	+8	+4

⑤ **Subtract.**

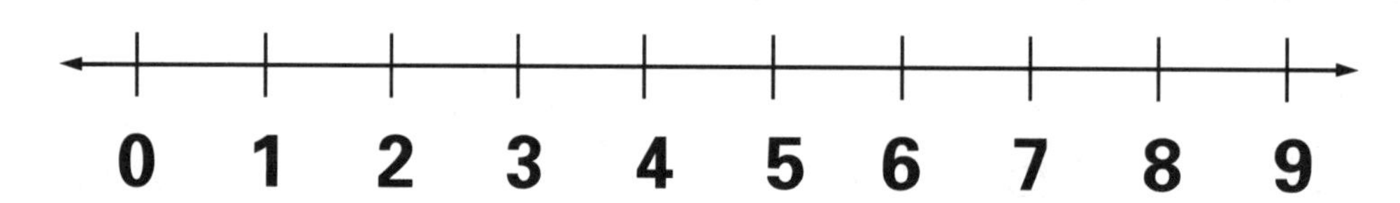

3	9	1	5	2	9
- 2	- 4	- 0	- 2	- 1	- 6

3	9	8	8
- 3	- 0	- 3	- 2

TEST 7

① Write the answers. 12 pts. total for this exercise.

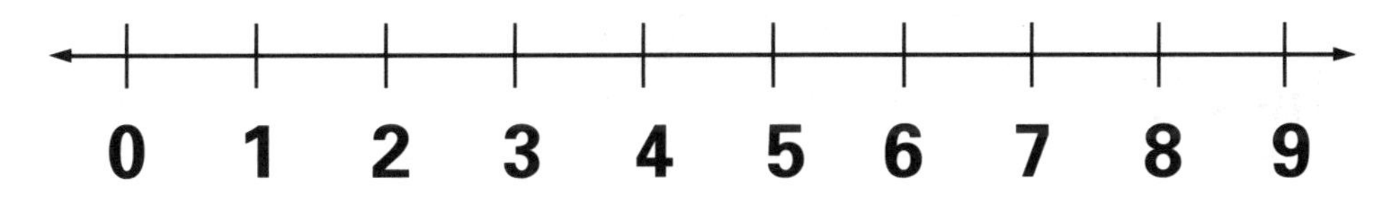

3	6	8	4	9	7
- 2	- 2	- 3	- 1	- 2	- 4

5	8	3	9	6	4
- 3	- 5	- 3	- 4	- 5	- 3

② Write the value of the coin. 6 pts. total for this exercise.

 ______¢  ______¢  ______¢

 ______¢  ______¢  ______¢

③ Brett counted 7 roses on the rose bush. Andy counted 8 more on another rose bush. How many roses were there altogether? 1 pt.

④ **Draw a line with the ruler.** **2 pts. total for this exercise.**

4 inches

•

3 inches

•

⑤ **Write the number.** **8 pts. total for this exercise.**

twenty-three	_____	sixty-eight	_____
seventy-nine	_____	thirty-four	_____
fifteen	_____	eighty-two	_____
ninety-one	_____	fifty-five	_____

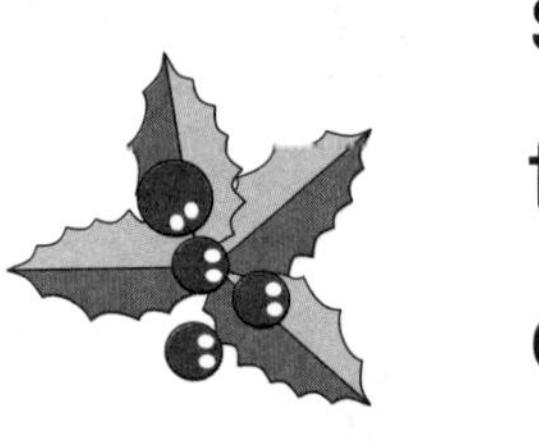

⑥ **Write the answers.** **12 pts. total for this exercise.**

1	5	9	1	3	2
8	3	1	6	2	4
+4	+3	+0	+5	+5	+1

14	46	23	65	53	15
+12	+32	+35	+23	+16	+20

41 pts. Total

NUMBER ORDER – ORDINAL NUMBERS

① Write the letters in the blanks.

____ ____ ____ ____ ____ ____ ____ ____

fourth	V	second	L	sixth	Y
first	I	eighth	U	seventh	O
fifth	E	third	O		

② How long is the path?

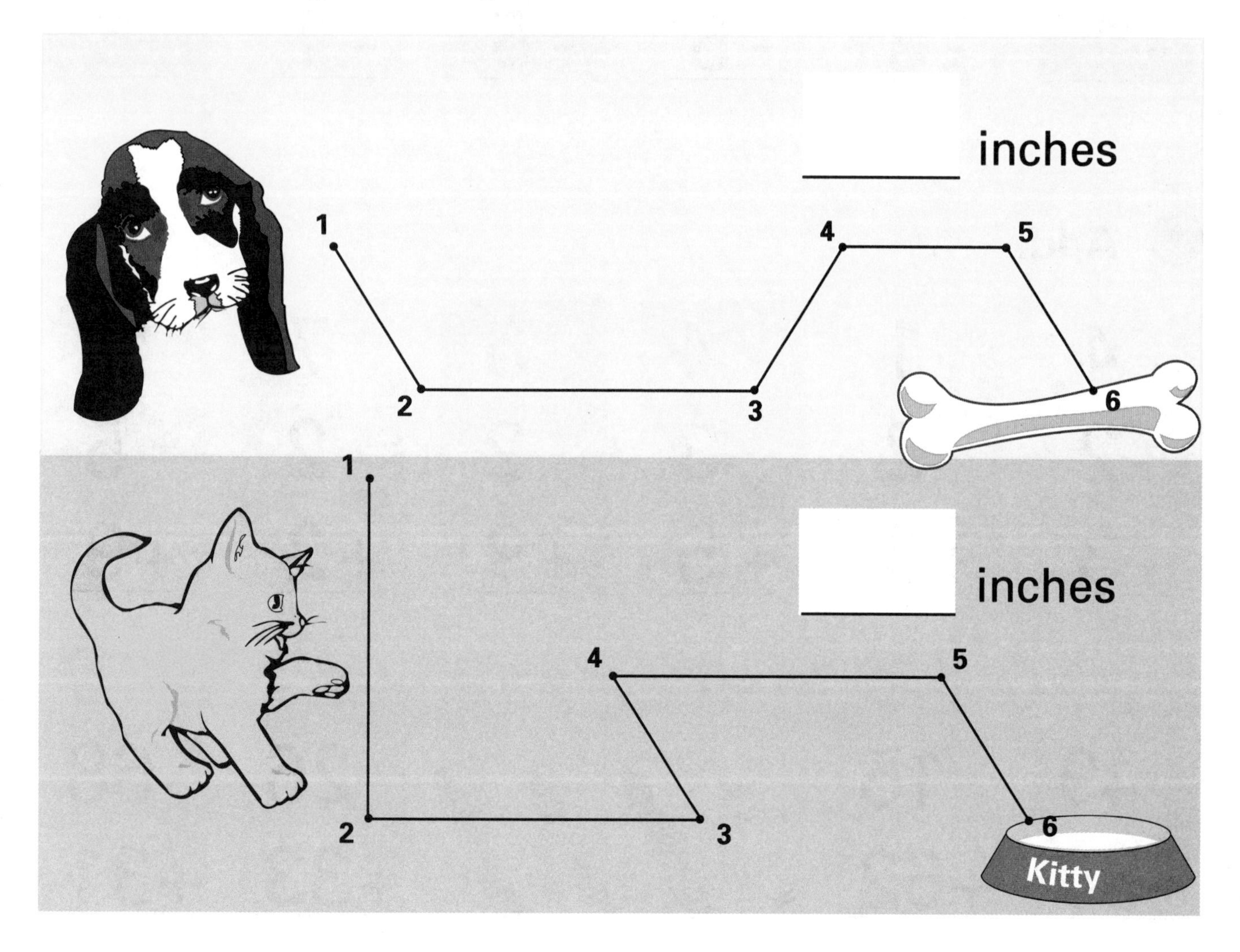

③ Subtract.

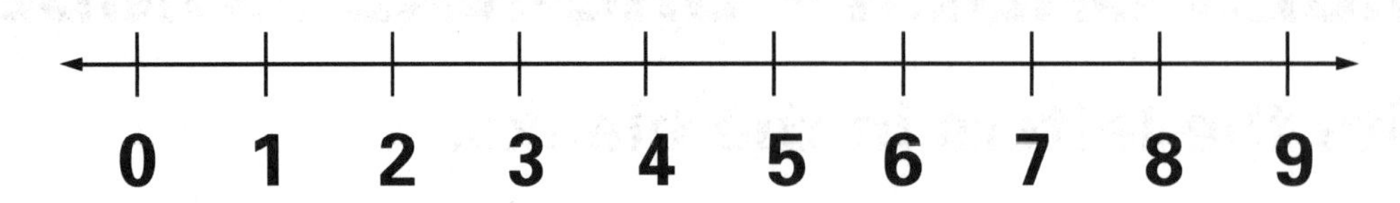

5	8	2	6	2	5
- 3	- 4	- 0	- 1	- 2	- 1

9	6	7	9	4	6
- 1	- 3	- 5	- 5	- 1	- 6

④ Add.

4	1	4	5	7	3
2	2	3	2	2	5
+3	+6	+5	+9	+2	+9

49	15	26	68
+30	+62	+33	+31

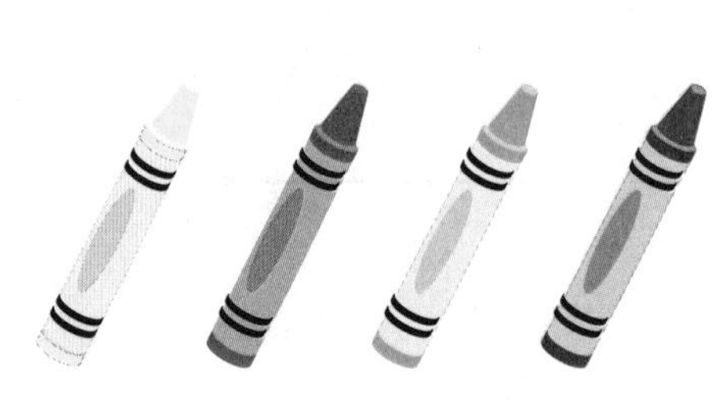

____

WORD PROBLEMS – SUBTRACTION

① Stan had 4 cookies in his lunch. He gave 1 of them to Glen. How many cookies did he have left?

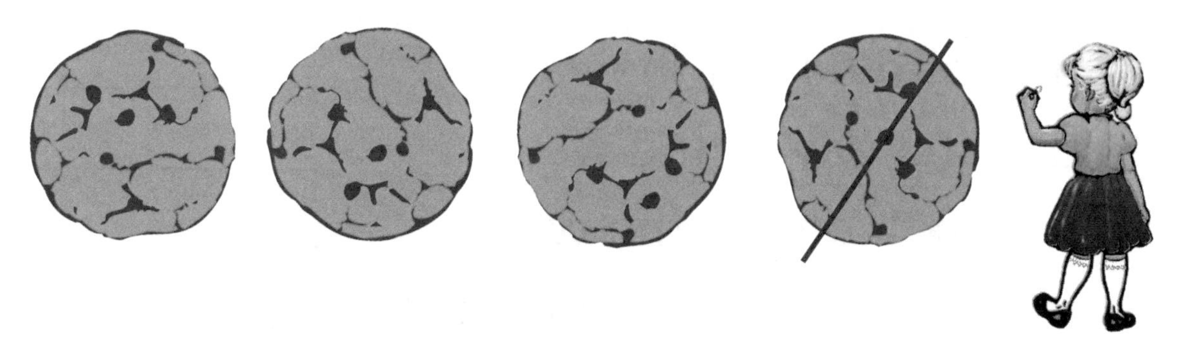

____ - ____ = ____ ________________

Wade had 8 marbles in his pocket. He gave 3 of them to Luke. How many marbles did he have left?

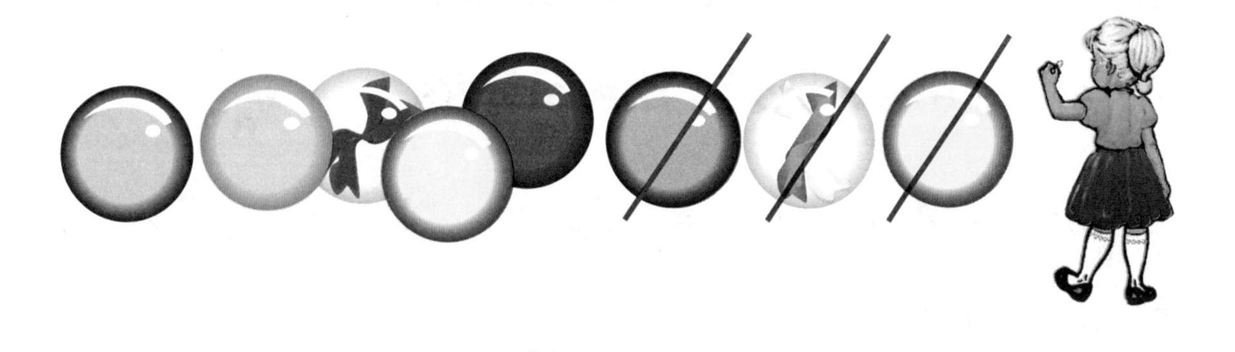

____ - ____ = ____ ________________

There were 7 birds on the fence. 2 of the birds flew away. How many birds were left on the fence?

____ - ____ = ____ ________________

② Sunday Monday Tuesday Wednesday Thursday Friday Saturday

Write the third day of the week. ____________

Write the first day of the week. ____________

Write the sixth day of the week. ____________

Write the seventh day of the week. ____________

Write the fifth day of the week. ____________

Write the fourth day of the week. ____________

Write the last day of the week. ____________

Write the middle day of the week. ____________

③ **Write the answers in the blanks.**

6 tens + 4 ones = 60 + 4 = 64

5 tens + 3 ones = ____ + ____ = ____

7 tens + 6 ones = ____ + ____ = ____

3 tens + 8 ones = ____ + ____ = ____

0 tens + 8 ones = ____ + ____ = ____

0 tens + 0 ones = ____ + ____ = ____

4 tens + 5 ones = ____ + ____ = ____

8 tens + 2 ones = ____ + ____ = ____

ADDITION AND SUBTRACTION

6+2=8	3+4=7	5+4=9
8-2=6	7-4=3	9-5=4
8-6=2	7-3=4	9-4=5

① **Write the subtraction facts.**

2+1=3 ____ ____

3+5=8 ____ ____

3+2=5 ____ ____

2+4=6 ____ ____

3+6=9 ____ ____

7+1=8 ____ ____

② **Write the numbers in the blanks.**

84 = ____ + ____

42 = ____ + ____

36 = ____ + ____

25 = ____ + ____

13 = ____ + ____ 8 = ____ + ____

79 = ____ + ____ 65 = ____ + ____

57 = ____ + ____ 91 = ____ + ____

③ **Add.**

6	4	2	6	5	2
2	3	3	2	3	4
+9	+5	+5	+5	+7	+7

④ **Subtract.**

5	7	9	8	7	6
- 4	- 0	- 6	- 5	- 7	- 5

8	6	7	5	8	9
- 1	- 3	- 4	- 2	- 0	- 2

PLACE VALUE

1 **Write the numbers.**

6 tens = ____ 7 tens = ____ 1 ten = ____

2 tens = ____ 3 tens = ____ 4 tens = ____

5 tens = ____ 8 tens = ____ 9 tens = ____

2 **Write the answers in the blanks.**

4+5= ____ -3 = ____ -4 = ____ +7= ____

2+5= ____ -2 = ____ +3= ____ -4= ____

3+2= ____ +4= ____ -4 = ____ -5= ____

1+4= ____ +3= ____ -7= ____ +6= ____

6+3= ____ -2 = ____ -3 = ____ +4= ____

2+4= ____ +3= ____ -5 = ____ +2= ____

3+4= ____ -5 = ____ +6= ____ -3= ____

3. Jason had 6 lollipops. He gave 2 of them to Ned. How many lollipops did he have left?

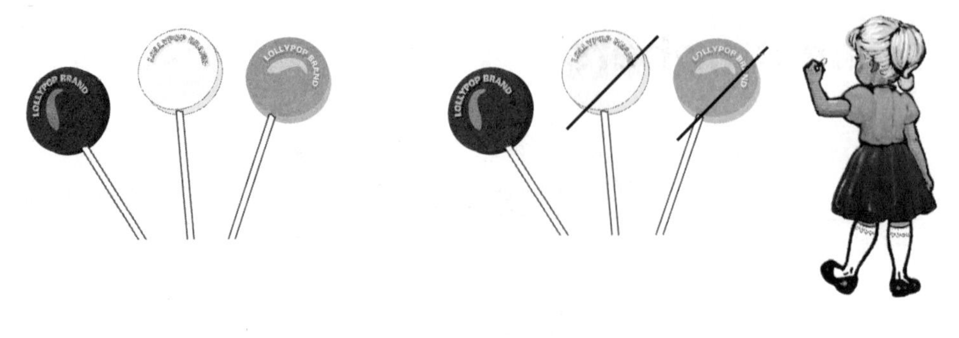

____ - ____ = ____ ________________

There were 9 squirrels in Joan's backyard. 4 of them climbed over the fence. How many were left in Joan's backyard?

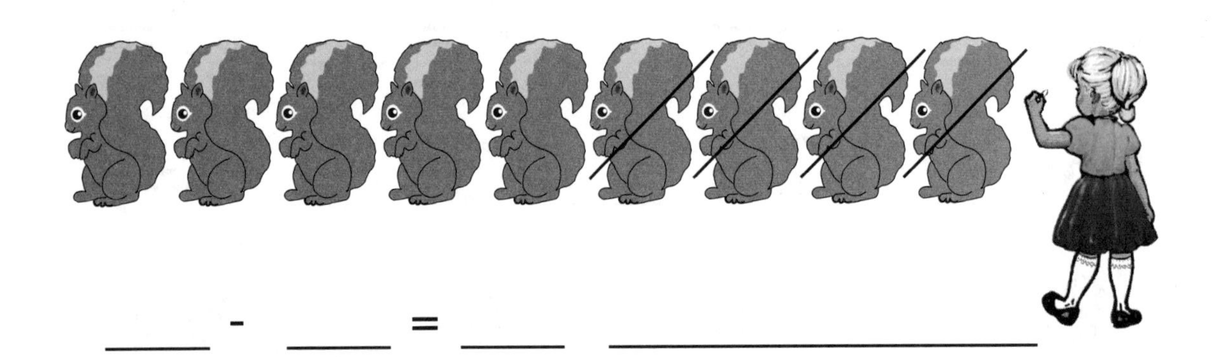

____ - ____ = ____ ________________

4. **Write the subtraction facts.**

$4+2=6$	$2+7=9$	$5+2=7$
________	________	________
________	________	________

TIME – HALF HOUR

① Write the correct time.

:

:

:

:

:

:

:

:

② Count the objects in each set. Write the number.

③ **Color the squares used in counting by 7's.**

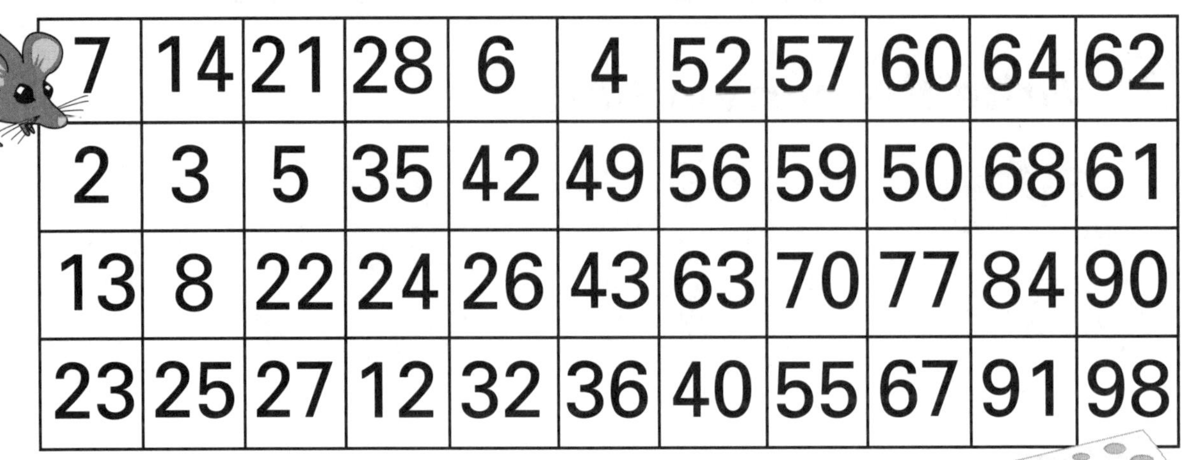

7	14	21	28	6	4	52	57	60	64	62
2	3	5	35	42	49	56	59	50	68	61
13	8	22	24	26	43	63	70	77	84	90
23	25	27	12	32	36	40	55	67	91	98

④ **Add.**

$$\begin{array}{r} 7 \\ 2 \\ +4 \\ \hline \end{array} \quad \begin{array}{r} 6 \\ 3 \\ +7 \\ \hline \end{array} \quad \begin{array}{r} 4 \\ 4 \\ +6 \\ \hline \end{array} \quad \begin{array}{r} 2 \\ 3 \\ +8 \\ \hline \end{array} \quad \begin{array}{r} 1 \\ 5 \\ +5 \\ \hline \end{array} \quad \begin{array}{r} 4 \\ 1 \\ +9 \\ \hline \end{array}$$

⑤ **Subtract.**

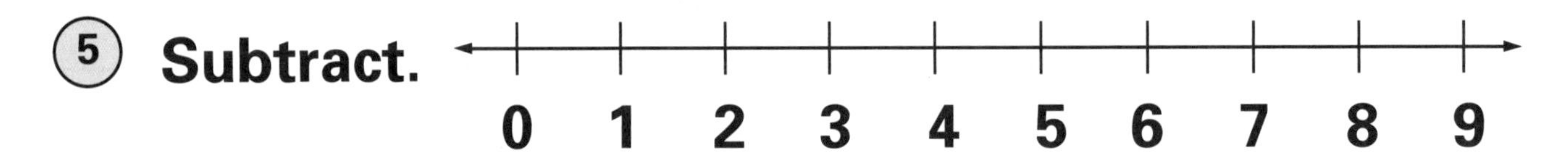

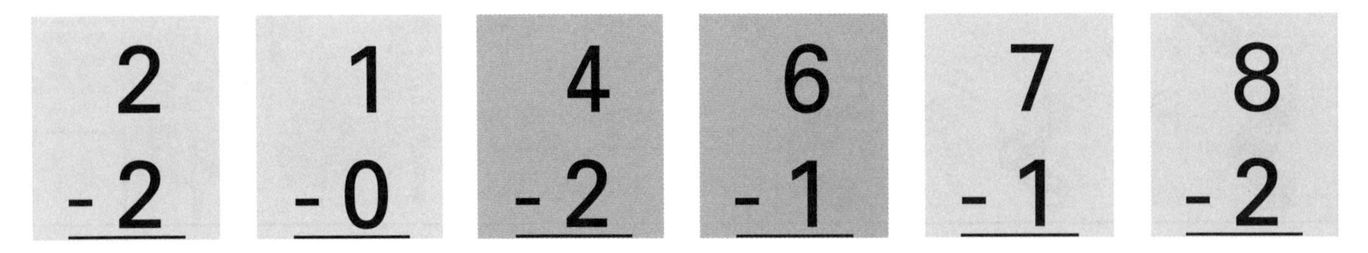

SHOW YOUR SKILLS

① **Draw the hour hand.**

② There were 7 crayons in Gary's desk. He gave 3 of them to Tony. How many crayons did Gary have left?

____ - ____ = ____ ________________

Carl had 6 postage stamps. He gave 4 of them to Eric. How many postage stamps did Carl have left?

____ - ____ = ____ ________________

③ Add.

21	25	22	60	83	31
+74	+32	+57	+35	+16	+64

4	4	5	6	7	5
5	2	1	2	0	2
+5	+8	+4	+4	+6	+5

④ Subtract.

0 1 2 3 4 5 6 7 8 9

7	6	5	3	4	8
- 6	- 2	- 5	- 1	- 0	- 3

4	9	7	8	9	2
- 3	- 5	- 0	- 6	- 3	- 2

SUBTRACTION 10-18

① **Subtract.**

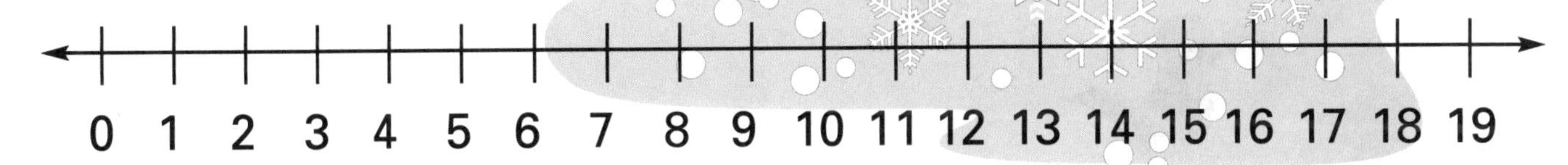

$10 - 3$	$11 - 2$	$13 - 9$	$10 - 5$	$12 - 3$	$14 - 7$
$15 - 6$	$10 - 8$	$13 - 5$	$17 - 8$	$11 - 4$	$12 - 6$
$11 - 6$	$12 - 4$	$14 - 5$	$16 - 9$	$18 - 9$	$13 - 6$
$10 - 1$	$11 - 5$	$11 - 9$	$12 - 7$	$14 - 8$	$15 - 8$

2 Circle the greater number.

3 Draw both hands on the clocks.

4 Count each set. Write the number.

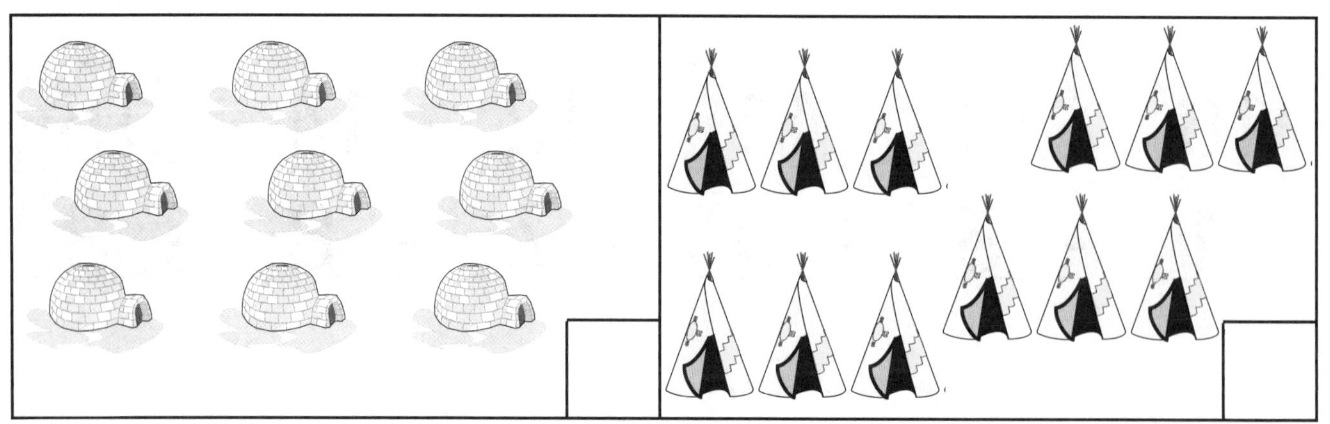

ADDITION – HORIZONTAL TO VERTICAL

① **Write the problems vertically. Add.**

$5 + 2 + 3 =$

$1 + 7 + 6 =$

$8 + 0 + 7 =$

$4 + 3 + 9 =$

$43 + 51 =$

$24 + 32 =$

② **Circle the number that is least.**

28 82

17 54

63 29

39 93

12 9

③ Subtract.

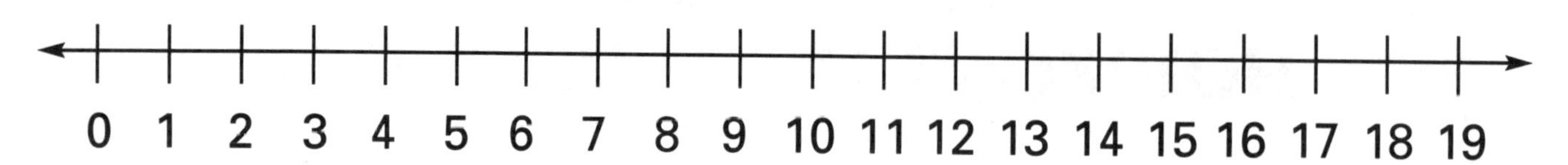

14 - 9	13 - 4	11 - 3	12 - 8	10 - 9	16 - 8
15 - 6	12 - 5	10 - 6	15 - 7	13 - 8	14 - 6
11 - 8	10 - 4	11 - 5	17 - 9	15 - 9	10 - 2

④ Write the next 3 even numbers.

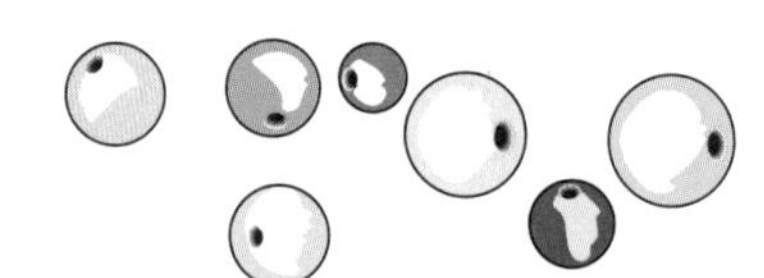

16 ___ ___ ___ 38 ___ ___ ___

24 ___ ___ ___ 74 ___ ___ ___

52 ___ ___ ___ 46 ___ ___ ___

WORD PROBLEMS – ADDITION

① There were 6 boys playing basketball. 2 more boys joined them. How many boys were now playing basketball?

Susan had 5 baby ducks. Toni gave her 3 more baby ducks. Susan now has how many baby ducks?

8 children were going up the hill to ride their sleds. 3 more children followed them up. How many children went up the hill to go sledding?

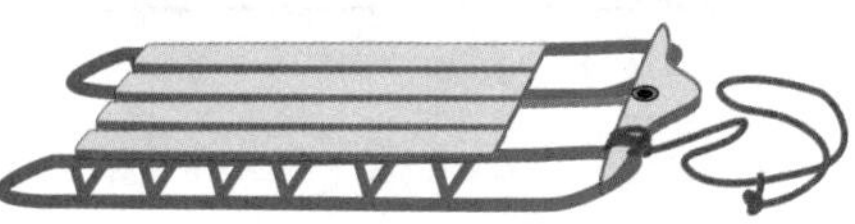

② **Write the next 3 numbers when counting by 8's.**

8 16 24 ____ ____ ____

48 56 64 ____ ____ ____

③ **Put an X on each shape that has one half ($\frac{1}{2}$) shaded.**

④ **Subract.**

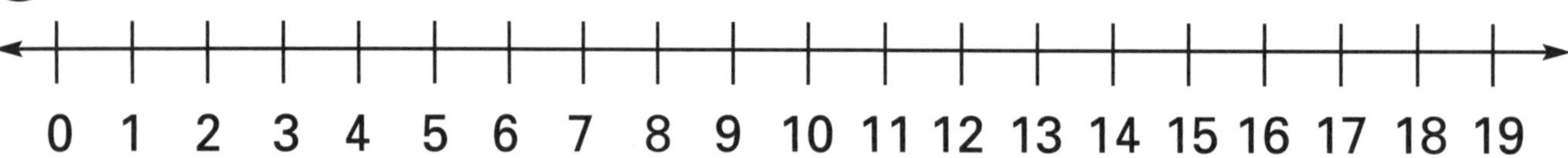

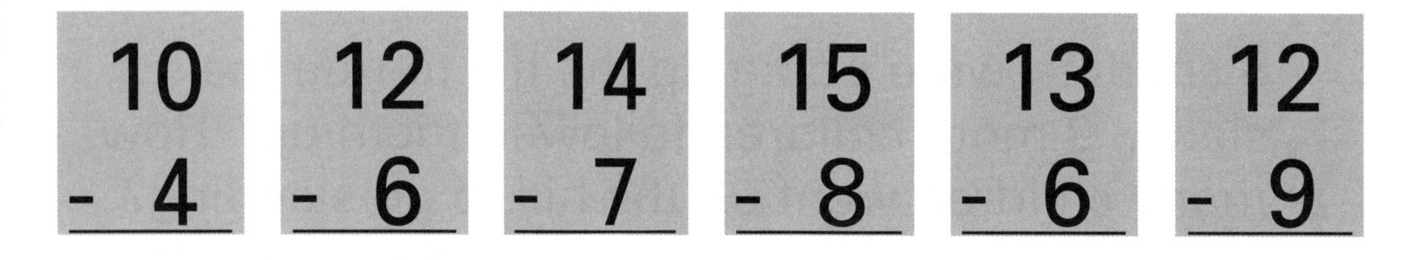

10	12	14	15	13	12
- 4	- 6	- 7	- 8	- 6	- 9

14	10	17	18	16	11
- 5	- 6	- 8	- 9	- 7	- 8

EQUAL AND NOT EQUAL

① **Write = or ≠ between each set.**

7-5 ___ 12	6-3 ___ 4	5-1 ___ 6
7-7 ___ 1	5-4 ___ 1	9-7 ___ 3
4-3 ___ 1	7-2 ___ 9	6-4 ___ 2
8-2 ___ 10	9-4 ___ 5	8-5 ___ 3
9-2 ___ 7	3-3 ___ 0	2-1 ___ 2

② **Put an X on each shape that has one fourth ($\frac{1}{4}$) shaded.**

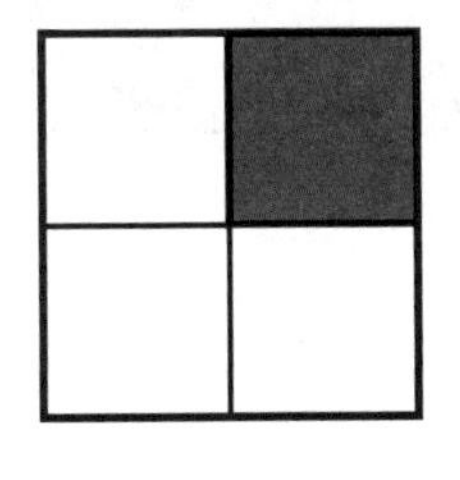
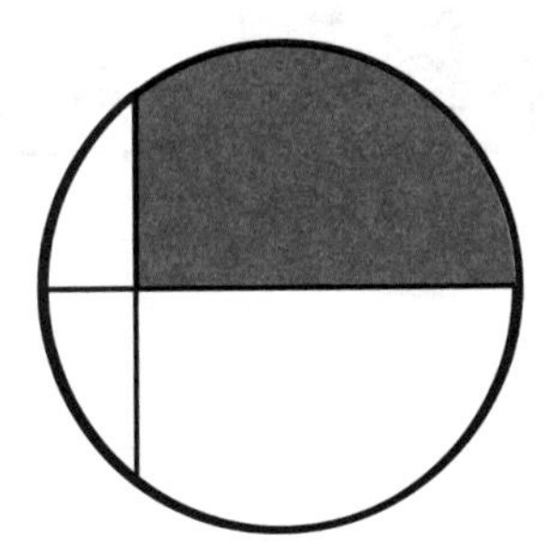
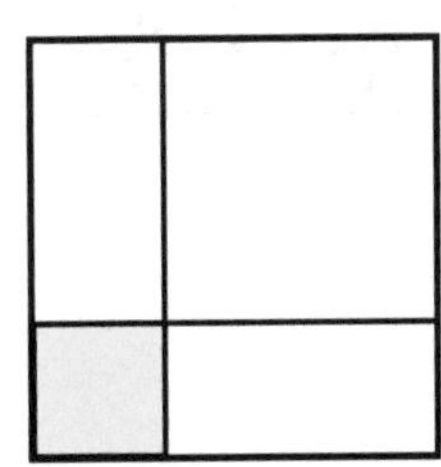
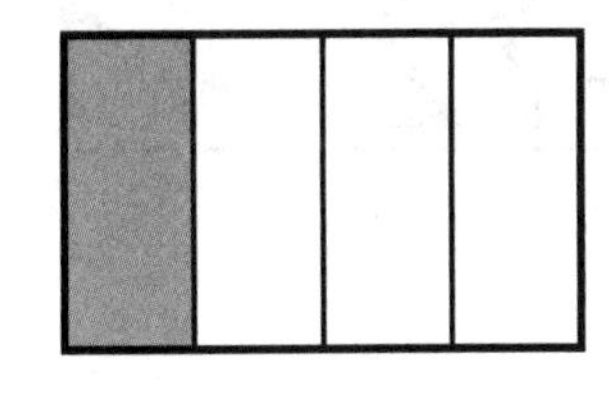

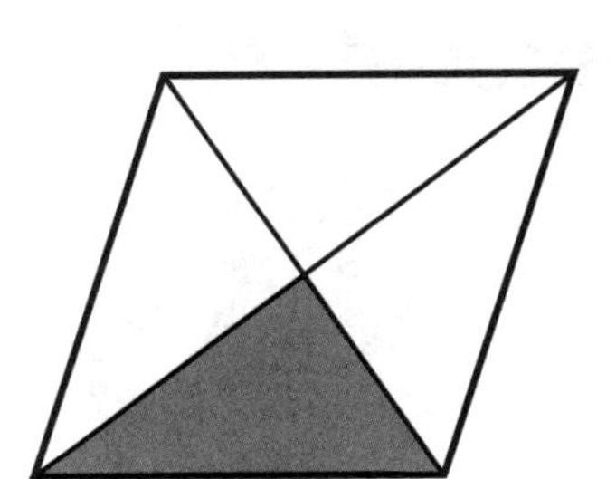
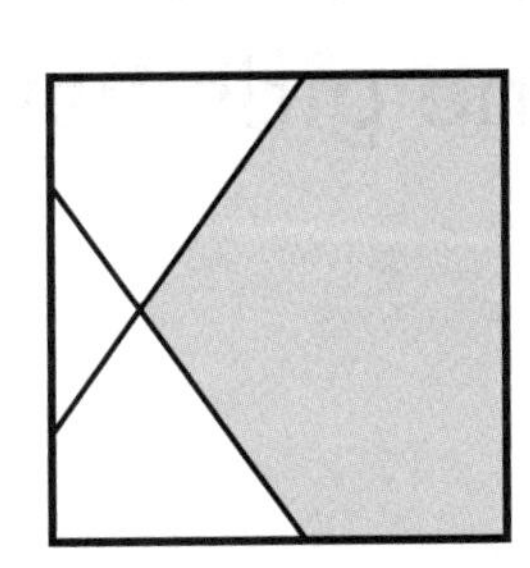
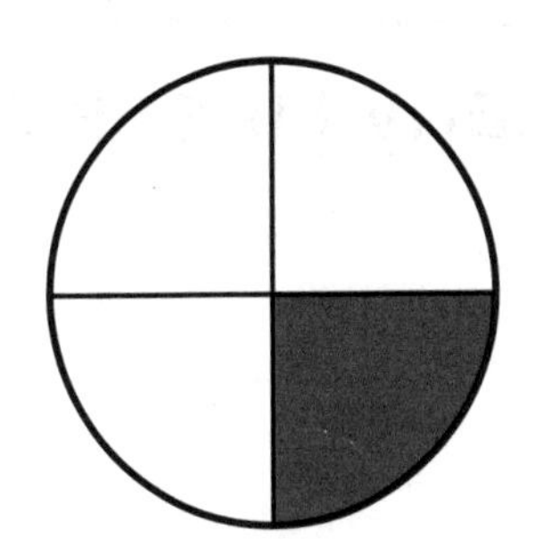
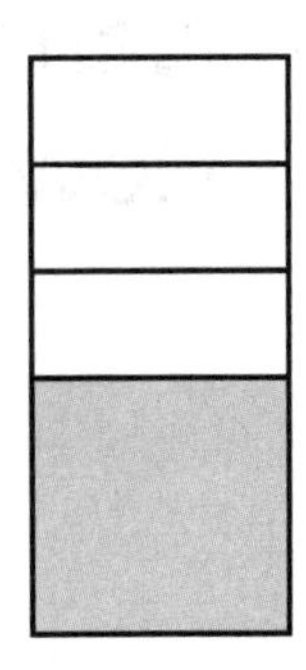

③ **Subtract.**

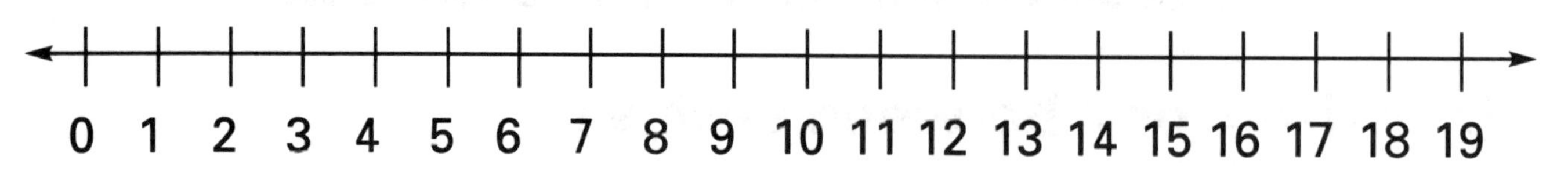

13	11	10	12	14	13
- 9	- 2	- 1	- 5	- 6	- 7

14	11	13	15	11	10
- 8	- 4	- 4	- 7	- 9	- 5

④ **Add.**

15	85	24	17	46	58
+72	+11	+33	+50	+12	+31

⑤ Nancy's cat had 7 kittens. Susie's cat had 3 kittens. How many kittens did the girls have altogether?

TEST 8

① **Circle the answer.** 6 pts.

Giraffe	fourth	fifth	sixth
Kitten	seventh	fifth	sixth
Bunny	first	second	third
Dog	fourth	fifth	sixth
Cow	first	second	seventh
Teddy Bear	fourth	fifth	sixth

② **Color the even numbered pictures.** 5 pts.

30

27

15

45

18

③ Write the problems vertically. Write the answers.

4 pts. total for this exercise.

$46 + 32 =$

$25 + 63 =$

$81 + 15 =$

$54 + 21 =$

④ Subtract. 12 pts. total for this exercise.

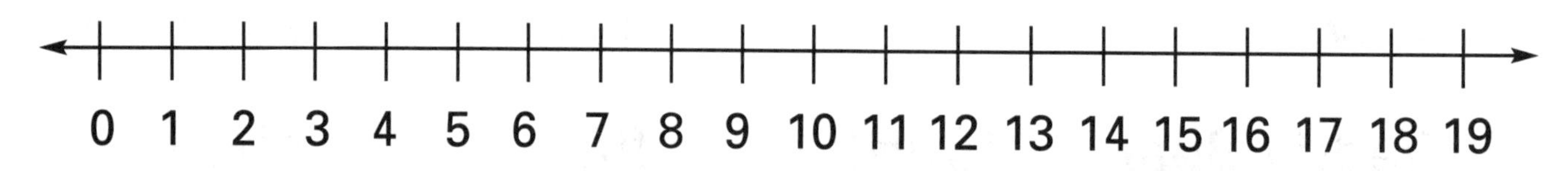

10	12	14	17	11	16
- 7	- 4	- 6	- 9	- 3	- 8

13	15	11	10	14	13
- 5	- 7	- 5	- 2	- 8	- 9

27 pts. Total

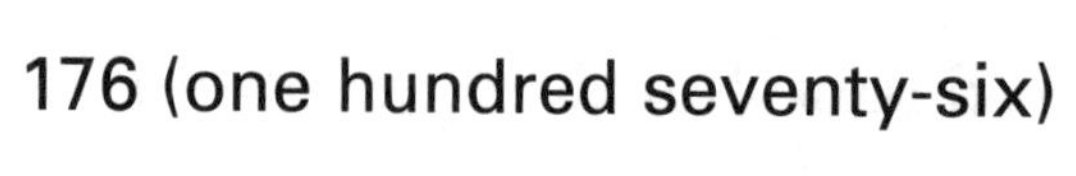

FRACTIONS – ONE THIRD

① **Put an X on each shape that has one third ($\frac{1}{3}$) shaded.**

② **Write = or ≠ between each set.**

$\frac{1}{2}$	_____	one half	43	_____	forty-four
$\frac{1}{3}$	_____	one fourth	78	_____	seventy-eight
$\frac{1}{4}$	_____	one third	65	_____	seventy-five
$\frac{1}{5}$	_____	one fifth	52	_____	forty-two
$\frac{1}{6}$	_____	one seventh	89	_____	ninety-eight

③ Subtract.

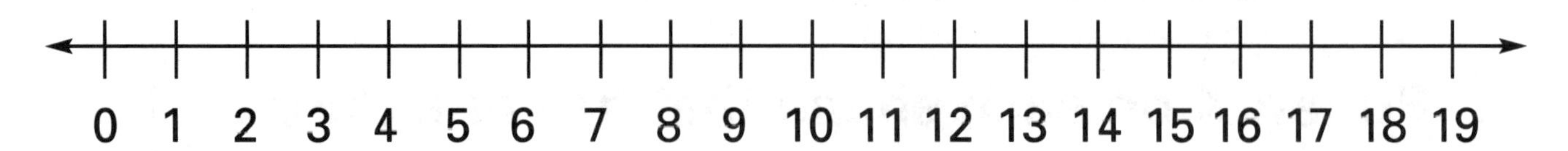

10	12	9	10	8	5
- 3	- 5	- 3	- 8	- 4	- 5

12	6	11	7	4	11
- 8	- 1	- 4	- 5	- 3	- 6

④ Write the correct letter in the blank.

___ 7 ___ 8 ___ 9 ___ 10 ___ 11

___ 12 ___ 13 ___ 14 ___ 15 ___ 16 ___ 17 ___ 18

P	L	A	A
6+3=	7+7=	8+9=	5+3=
Y	D	H	H
7+4=	9+7=	8+4=	4+3=
O	Y	I	P
8+5=	9+9=	6+9=	8+2=